Solveig Dahl

Rape –
A Hazard to Health

Solveig Dahl

Rape –
A Hazard to Health

Scandinavian
University Press

Scandinavian University Press (Universitetsforlaget AS), 0608 Oslo
Distributed world-wide excluding Norway by
Oxford University Press, Walton Street, Oxford OX2 6DP

Oxford   New York   Toronto
Delhi   Bombay   Calcutta   Madras   Karachi
Kuala Lumpur   Singapore   Hong Kong   Tokyo
Nairobi   Dar es Salaam   Cape Town
Melbourne   Auckland   Madrid
and associated companies in Berlin   Ibadan

Oxford is a trade mark of Oxford University Press

Published in the United States
by Oxford University Press Inc., New York

© Universitetsforlaget 1993

Cover illustration:
© Frans Widerberg / BONO 1993
«Sjelen forlater sitt døde legeme»
("The soul departing from its dead body") 1976
Oil 114x145 cm

Published with a grant from the Norwegian Research Council for Science and the
Humanities

British Library Cataloguing in Publication Data
Data available

ISBN 82-00-21809-0

Library of Congress Cataloguing in Publication Data
Data available

Typeset by Paston Press Ltd, Norwich, UK
Printed in Norway by A/S Foto-Trykk, Trøgstad, 1993

Contents

Foreword

My interest in the link between sexual assault and mental health started in clinical work. During the late 1960s and early 1970s, when I was training as a psychotherapist and psychiatrist, the effect of traumatic experiences in adolescent and adult life aroused little interest. I became aware of the importance of mental trauma while engaged in psychotherapeutic work with women, couples and families. During the course of exploring symptoms, pains and interpersonal problems, information would emerge regarding for instance the experience of a rape ordeal and its effect. In this way, the plight of the patients made me reflect on relationships that I had learned little about during my training.

In 1984, when the Rape Tribunal was held in Oslo, Kirsti Malterud, a general practitioner, decided to look into the public health service's attitude towards rape victims and their need for medical services. She engaged two physicians, Lisbeth Bang and Kitty Strand, to collaborate on the report "Medical services for rape victims in Oslo. A report on the public health service's possibilities, limitations and obligations" (Bang et al, 1984). In their conclusion, attention was drawn to the poor treatment, even negligence, accorded rape victims by the public health authorities, and the idea was launched for a plan to organize medical services to deal with the health problems of rape victims. The report was prepared for the Oslo Board of Health and was delivered to the Chief Medical Officer in Oslo. I was contacted by the group and invited to join a new commission appointed by the Chief Medical Officer to draw up a plan of action for a medical service for rape victims in Oslo. My task was to formulate a plan for the psychosocial part of the service. The plan of action, delivered to the Chief Medical Officer in June 1985, proposed that a rape admission service for the city of Oslo be situated at the municipal Oslo Emergency Ward (OEW). The service would be integrated with the general medical crisis facility at the ward.

Within psychiatric research in Norway there existed a group of psychiatrists whose major concern focused on psychological traumas and psychosocial consequences; the Division of Disaster Psychiatry at Gaustad Hospital. This research group was also aware of the still limited knowledge about the effects of traumas caused by violence. This was one of the reasons why Professor Emeritus Leo Eitinger, following his retirement, became a valuable associate of the unit. His pioneer investigation of concentration camp victims, his commitment to torture victims and his attitude towards victims of violence in general, were of great importance to the group. The Division had been gathering information on the effects of violence-produced traumas from a study of UN soldiers in peacekeeping service (Weisæth and Sund, 1982), from work with hostages, bank and post office employees exposed to violence (Eitinger and Weisæth, 1981), and from examinations of 13 Norwegian seamen who had been exposed to torture in Libya (Weisæth, 1989). In addition, during the autumn of 1984, Sverre Varvin, a psychiatrist, carried out a pilot investigation at Oslo Police Headquarters on victims of criminal violence (1986) and the Division wanted to carry out a more extensive study. Rape victims were considered to be an important group among victims of criminal violence. I signalled my interest. The project was originally defined as a study of several kinds of victims of criminal violence. Unfortunately, we obtained enough funds for only one researcher and the project had to be curtailed. The Oslo Board of Health and later Ullevål Hospital gave me leave from my position as medical director at Østensjø Family Clinic. This was a condition for my working with the project.

At every stage of my work, I have received valuable assistance and support. The main contributors have been the Division of Disaster Psychiatry at Gaustad Hospital and, particularly, Professor Lars Weisæth, who was the main supervisor of the project. His enthusiasm, optimism and loyal belief in the project meant a lot to me throughout.

Professor Emeritus Leo Eitinger, whose interest, advice and support were invaluable during the whole period should also be mentioned specifically. Professor Ulrik Malt contributed extra advice when needed, particularly on methodology and choice of instruments. Later, Karsten Hytten, who for part of the time was a fellow researcher at the Division, helped as a second scorer for the reliability testing. Other members of the Division also contributed at our meetings and mutual discussions. Another important contributor at Gaustad Hospital was the librarian Målfrid Framnes.

The municipal Emergency Ward in Oslo, the general health section as well as the social emergency and psychiatric emergency unit, co-operated from the start, and accepted me as one of the staff. Nothing would have come of this project had they not given me their trust and co-operation. I am, of course, even more grateful to the participants in this study for sharing their experiences and suffering with me.

The data collection period lasted for more than two years, from January 1986 to February 1988. In this period Professor of Psychology Hanne Haavind joined in as a supervisor of the qualitative research. She was willing and able not only to give me some idea of the principles of qualitative research, but also to listen to the rape-event narratives and thereby share the stress of the interviews with me. From the start of my project she also introduced me to a transprofessional group (psychologists, physicians, sociologists) of female researchers whose main interest was women's research, and later to a specific group of researchers working with projects concerning violence against women. Discussions in these groups have also been important along the way.

In the preparation and coding of data for computer processing and the statistical analysis of the data, a major supporter was the statistician, Leiv Sandvik, whose patience, valuable assistance and advice saw me through a difficult period.

The final period was dominated by the writing of this monograph. Professor Astri Nøkleby Heiberg volunteered to act as an assistant supervisor, a task mistress and supporter, and I am extremely grateful for her contribution. Several others offered criticism and suggestions when the final version was drafted and I am indebted to all of them.

Funding of the research project was provided by the Norwegian Research Council for Science and the Humanities (NAVF), mainly by the Council for Medical Research (RMF), but later also by the Council for Social Services (RSF). Funding was also given, twice, by the Solveig and Johan P. Sommers' Foundations for the Advancement of Psychiatric Research.

I am indebted to Chris Ennals for his help with the English language in the draft version.

My husband, Carl-Ivar, has been my primary supporter with his willingness to listen, read, give advice, keep his mouth shut and tolerate a from time-to-time mute and extremely distracted companion. I am very grateful for his contribution.

Oslo, 25 June 1992

1

The Aims and Background of the Study

1.1 The Aims

The aims of the present study were to:

(1) investigate rape as a psychological stressor by exploring the traumatic event and seek to identify which elements of the ordeal are felt as particularly stressful to the victim;
(2) identify the nature of health problems which might develop after exposure to rape, both in the acute phase and as long-term problems – in this context, the main interest was to identify the nature of mental health problems and particularly the presence of Post-Traumatic Stress Disorder;
(3) investigate how the psychological reaction to rape changes in the course of the first year and look for differences within the victim group;
(4) investigate whether any factors which can be identified in the acute phase may predict a risk of developing long-term mental health problems;
(5) explore how the psychological experience of rape and subsequent reactions influence the victim's perception of self and her relationship to others;
(6) explore differences in coping within the victim group, and the association between coping strategy and recovery;
(7) investigate whether there are any changes in somatic health pre- and post-assault and whether such changes are associated with changes in mental health.

1.2 The Background

The background factors which will be presented in relation to the present study concern three issues:

(1) theoretical considerations concerning the meaning of rape as
     well as theories on how traumatic experiences might lead to
     health problems. I have assumed that these considerations
     might be helpful in throwing light on the results in this study. I
     hope this in turn will contribute to making the results more
     applicable to clinical practice.
(2) earlier empirical research concerning the psycho-social conse-
     quences of rape. This research is presented to the extent that it
     is relevant for comparison with the present study and for the
     development of the research questions raised here.
(3) the history and functioning of the context in which the research
     took place.

1.2.1. THEORETICAL CONSIDERATIONS

1.2.1.1. The Confusion Surrounding the Issue of Rape

The interpretation and meaning of a rape event are not a straightforward matter. The issue is confusing for several reasons:

(1) It is linked to issues of male domination in general and in sexual
     relations in particular.
(2) It is linked to understanding the general effects of sexual assault
     on all women's development and behaviour.
(3) It is linked to an understanding of human destructiveness,
     cultural attitudes concerning violence and how people deal with
     the unpleasant knowledge of this destructiveness by blaming
     the victim.
(4) It is linked to an understanding of the connection between sex
     and violence and the eroticization of both power and violence
     and of subordination.

Male domination in the sexual sphere is connected not only to men's
potential for physical dominance, but also to cultural beliefs and
attitudes concerning sexual relations. Traditionally, men have been
the possessors of desire, women the objects of men's desire, the
passive receivers. Modern sexology has challenged these assump-
tions by drawing attention to the old forgotten knowledge that
women's orgasmic capacity is impressive (Masters and Johnson,
1970). Women as passive receivers who are expected to signal
willingness become easy targets for projective interpretation.

Women are accused of signalling willingness when they are not aware of it. The problem is that when they try to correct the impression this is not taken seriously. "When a woman says no, she means yes," and similar slogans confuse the picture.

In a study on cultural myths and support for rape, Burt finds that rape myth attitudes are strongly connected to sex role stereotyping, distrust of the opposite sex and acceptance of interpersonal violence (Burt, 1980). Rape can also be seen as an extreme of the dominance/subordination pattern in sexual relations, an extreme that goes far beyond sadomasochistic practice where mutual consent represents an important rule (Ehrenreich et al, 1987).

Aggression in relations between the sexes does not represent aggression between equal partners, but is linked to men's potential for physical dominance. The knowledge of this and the threat of bodily violation may influence women's socialization. One solution can be to seek a male protector, a man whose physical strength and status will be respected by another male and thus serve as a defence (Brownmiller, 1974). Other solutions are to deny or control the danger by treating men as equals, by trustful subordination or by seeking influence over them through erotic power. When such counteraction fails, for instance when protectors become aggressors, or potential friends or lovers become offenders, the woman not only appears naive, but her failed strategy might easily lead to a breakdown in her construction of reality and consequently to chaos and confusion.

Research has shown that the fear of violence and rape has a restricting effect on women's behaviour (Rieger and Gordon, 1981; Burt and Esteep, 1981). The view that fear of sexual assault by men influences women's development has, however, hardly been touched upon in developmental psychology.

In Western culture, attitudes towards violence are ambiguous: violence is both condemned and admired. The victim is pitied, but also despised. Violence is condemned as an instrument of illegal goals, accepted as an instrument of law and order and sometimes admired and glorified in the hands of the hero. Thus, historically, rape has been illegal when the goal was bad, namely stealing another man's property, but legal as the husband's right to possess and control his wife's body. It has been accepted as the natural behaviour of the Greek gods and beautified in art, as in Rubens' picture "The Rape of the Sabine Women" (Metzger, 1976).

Blaming the victim is probably a complex phenomenon. It may consist of elements like contempt for the weak, a need to believe in a just world and a defence against a realization that we may all become victims. By blaming the victim and focusing on what is wrong with her, the illusion of invulnerability can be maintained. This tendence is not only displayed in relation to rape, but is a general tendency in relation to all victims of human aggression (Eitinger, 1985). But blaming as well as self-blame in victims of rape might also be related to a view more explicit in traditional male-dominated cultures where women are brought up to think they are responsible for violations of their sexual boundaries, even if they lack the power to protect themselves (Agger, 1992).

The boundary between sex and violence is also complicated by the eroticization of power and violence as well as of subordination. Sexual fantasies about rape, not only in men but also in women, might also serve as justification for rape, the argument being that women are masochistic and like it. The victim involved is not asked: her reality is defined by the offenders. A fantasy is controlled by the beholder and can never be compared to or experienced as anything similar to an uncontrolled attack. The psychoanalyst Helene Deutsch viewed women's rape fantasies as their attempt to adapt to and cope with the painful aspects of feminine sexuality, i.e. an attempt to control the uncontrollable (Hartman, 1984).

Andenæs, a leading Norwegian professor of law, claimed that the aim of rape is primarily satisfaction of an "in itself normal drive" (Andenæs, 1974). Research on offenders does not confirm that this "normal drive" is a simple sexual drive. Groth, who conducted a study of convicted rapists, states: "Rape is a Pseudosexual Act, a pattern of sexual behaviour that is concerned much more with status, hostility, control and dominance than with sensual pleasure or sexual satisfaction. It is sexual behaviour in the primary service of non-sexual needs" (Groth, 1977). The regular occurrence of rape in war and its use as a method of political torture also supports Groth's statement (Brownmiller, 1974; Agger, 1989). However, to say that rape is not sexuality is also confusing since sexual behaviour is so strongly involved. One has to take into account that violence, power and subordination can be eroticized and acted out in sexual behaviour to the extent that vital and mutual rules for human interaction are violated.

The intention in pointing out the confusion surrounding the issue of rape is to focus on the difficulty of assessing and interpreting the meaning of the traumatic event. There is no single theory which will explain to us what rape means psychologically to a woman. Confusion and thus ambiguity could be a starting point.

1.2.1.2. Theories on the Transformation of Traumatic Experiences into Mental Health Problems

Early theories. The relationship between neurosis and traumatic events has been explained both psychologically and physiologically. Briquet (1859) explained hysterical symptoms (dissociation and conversion) as a result of a traumatic event that affected the brain's ability to process emotions (van der Kolk, 1987). Charcot also believed that hysterical symptoms were caused by brain changes after a traumatic event (van der Kolk, 1987).

Freud had a psychological explanation and interpreted the cognitive, emotional and behavioural symptoms of his hysterical patients as symbolic repetitions of early traumatic events. He believed that the memory of a traumatic event which was unbearable and charged with conflict was repressed and sealed off from the rest of the personality. The memory could be activated by associative events and elicit the psychopathological symptoms (Freud, 1896). Freud focused on childhood sexual traumas as an aetiological factor, but then abandoned this theory in favour of forbidden childhood sexual fantasies (Freud, 1905). After the First World War, Freud described external traumas as aetiological factors in war neurosis (Freud, 1920). He also described the compulsion to repeat the trauma, in thoughts, dreams and sometimes action, as a coping mechanism. But he also believed that the hyper-reactivity to external stimuli found in these patients had a biological explanation: the physical fixation to the trauma resulted from a break in the stimulus barrier experienced during severe shock (Freud, 1920).

From 1889 on, the French psychiatrist Pierre Janet also explored the psychological processes involved in the transformation of traumatic experiences into psychopathology. His psychological theories included descriptions of how experiences were normally mentally integrated and processed as memories. He described how in ordinary circumstances people automatically integrate new information and how the incoming data are organized and categorized in the light of previous integrated memories.

Janet proposed that memories could be stored on various levels, as narratives, sensory perceptions, visual images and "visceral" sensations. Janet believed that under ordinary conditions consciousness consists of a unified memory of all psychological facets related to a particular experience. Memories of frightening experiences not fitting into existing cognitive schemata could, however, be split off from conscious awareness and fragments of unintegrated events could then later turn up as pathological automatisms, intruding as terrifying perceptions, obsessional preoccupations and somatic re-experiences. Janet believed that what interfered with the integration of experiences was above all the intense emotions accompanying the traumatic events. He postulated an inverse relationship between the intensity of the emotional reaction and the capacity to process traumatic memories conceptually. He also thought that the physiological response in vehement emotion accounted for the continued emergency response to subsequent stresses; this would mean that a biological change took place too.

Janet's work has been the subject of renewed interest in the last few years. His observation of memory processing and how the mind can dissociate in the face of overwhelming threat, his observation of the tendency to react automatically with excessive emotion to subsequent stressors, his description of visceral, perceptual, emotional or motor symptoms as evidence that elements of the trauma are being involuntarily re-lived, and amnesia and constricted affect as ways to avoid dealing with traumatic memories have been rediscovered in modern cognitive psychology, neurobiology and contemporary psychiatry, especially in relation to the symptoms of Post-Traumatic Stress Disorder (PTSD; see definition in Chapter 2) (van der Kolk and van der Hart, 1989).

Another psychophysiological model was Pavlov's description of classical conditioning, which simply described how a strong unconditioned stimulus (e.g. an environmental threat) elicited an intense physiological response, and how, later on, cues associated with the aversive event could elicit the same response; the response now becomes conditioned.

Classical conditioning involves learning by association. Another component added later in behavioural theory is the concept of instrumental learning, the principle that, when aversive conditioning occurs, the organism will behave in any way necessary to avoid the aversive stimuli (Keane et al., 1985).

Crisis theory is concerned with the short-term breakdown of adaptation in relation to sudden changes in life where earlier experiences and problem-solving strategies are not sufficient to deal with the situation. The crisis reaction is characterized by emotional imbalance, feelings of helplessness, anxiety and despair (Caplan, 1961, 1964; Cullberg, 1981). Crisis reactions elicited by traumatic events are called traumatic crises (Cullberg, 1981). Crisis reactions are considered to be short term, lasting from six to eight weeks. The term "crisis" has been closely connected with ideas of preventive psychiatry and early intervention, crisis intervention (Caplan, 1964). In relation to traumatic events, crisis theory has been helpful in understanding the immediate response of victims in the acute phase and in providing a model for early intervention to prevent long-term psychiatric consequences.

Stress theory. Theories and research concerning stress are also closely related to the study of traumatic events and to the description of crises. The founder of stress research, Seyle, focuses on the biological response to incidents, or agents, that demand adaptive measures from the organism. He defines stress as the result of any demand upon the body, be the effect mental or somatic. The agents or demands are referred to as stressors (Seyle, 1982). Modern research on psychological stress was stimulated by the desire to understand breakdowns in adaptive behaviour observed in extreme situations, such as, military combat, concentration camps, bereavement (Holroyd and Lazarus, 1982). The research on biological changes following extreme stress caused by serious threats has been used to explain most of the symptoms of Post-Traumatic Stress Disorder (van der Kolk, 1990). However, the stress research field covers both biological research and psychological research on cognitive processes. The information process theorists are concerned with how thought processes such as attention, registration, problem-solving and memory storage are disturbed in states of autonomic arousal accompanied by intense emotion, such as fear (Hamilton, 1982). Appraisal theorists have mainly been concerned with the evaluation and interpretation of the stressful event and how the meaning attached to the event may influence the response (Folkman et at, 1979).

Cognitive theorists also emphasize coping as a moderator of stress. The term "coping" describes the individual effort both to manage the demands of the traumatic event as well as to moderate the emotional response. Coping is closely connected to appraisal: the choice of coping strategy will be influenced by how an event is appraised and the choice of coping strategy will in turn influence further appraisal (Folkman et al., 1979).

How an event is appraised is not just an individual matter, but a question of how an event is interpreted in the culture, or within a social context. This will influence the individual appraisal of the event as well as the response from others. Social networks and support systems have proved to be an extremely valuable coping resource (Folkman et al. 1979). In a Norwegian study of coping in families with handicapped children, Ingstad and Sommerschild (1983) describe the cultural meanings ascribed to stressful events and propose that normally there exist different "cultural codes" for how an event should be coped with, which will be reflected in the individual and family coping strategy.

In relation to rape, cultural attitudes and beliefs are of particular importance given the confusing and ambiguous attitudes surrounding such an event. Thus difficulties in coping with rape and subsequent long-term health problems might be connected, not only to an appraisal and experience of danger, but to multiple cognitions and emotions. It is also likely that the victim of rape experiences less support from the social network than someone involved in traumas that are accepted as stressors and where there is more consensus about the meaning of the event.

1.2.2. EARLIER EMPIRICAL RESEARCH OF RELEVANCE TO THE PRESENT STUDY

1.2.2.1. Epidemiology

The epidemiology of rape is not a simple question for the following reasons:

(1) Official records of crime rates are influenced by the accuracy and completeness of record-keeping by police officers; these might vary owing to different attitudes, priorities and workload (Rabkin, 1979).
(2) Under-reporting of crimes is believed to be a problem in general, and under-reporting of sexual offences is believed to be particularly high (Rabkin, 1979).
(3) Survey figures will depend upon how the information is obtained (e.g. questionnaires or interviews) and how the questions are formulated (e.g. descriptions of certain acts, classified by the researcher as rape, or direct questions about being raped).
(4) Some women (men) have been victims of several incidents of rape and sexual assault; that means the incidence and prevalence of the crime are not the same as the number of victims.

In the USA there have been several studies of life-time prevalence of rape and attempted rape. The results vary for adult women
from 44 percent (Russel, 1983) to 9 percent (Kilpatrick, 1986). The
number reporting the offence to the police also varied: in Russel's
study it was 8 percent, in Kilpatrick's study 30 percent. The method
in Russel's study took the form of long personal interviews, while
Kilpatrick made use of telephone interviews. Both researchers
relied not just on questions about rape, but also on descriptions of
acts which would meet the legal definition of rape. Russel's study
also estimated a yearly incidence of 3 percent. This is not far from
the results in a questionnaire survey of students, which found an
incidence rate for the last six months prior to the study to be 38 per
1,000 (Koss et al., 1987). The life-time prevalence in this study was
27.5 percent.

Even if the American figures had been consistent, they cannot be
directly applied in Norway. Amir pointed out that rape is linked to
an overall pattern of violence in society (Amir, 1971). If this is the
case, Norwegian figures should be lower than figures from the US.
In criminal statistics for Norway for the period 1983–87 there was an
increase in police reported rapes from 175–288 a year for the whole
country. This figure is very low.

In a Norwegian study conducted by Berit Schei on a random
sample of 118 Norwegian women aged 20–50, 6 percent had
experienced forced sex through violence, force or threat of force by
their spouse after the age of 18. Another 3 percent had experienced
forced sex through interpersonal coercion by a violent spouse
(implicit threat), and 5 percent reported rapes in other kinds of
victim–offender relationships, half of them strangers and half of
them acquaintances. Since the categories were not mutually exclus-
ive, the total life-time prevalence was 13 percent (Schei, 1990). In
exploring assaults by a spouse, Schei did not use the word rape, but
asked for a description of the acts. In other relationships she used
the term rape. Schei's findings indicate that rape in intimate
relationships are more frequent than rapes in relationships with
more distant acquaintances or strangers, especially when one takes
into account the fact that rapes in partner relationships are often
repeated. Schei's study does not state how many had reported the
assaults to the police, nor does she report any incidence figures. The
participation rate in the study was 90 percent. The women were
interviewed in depth as a comparison group in a study of physical
and sexual abuse by spouse as a risk factor in gynaecological
disorders and adverse perinatal outcome. The results were to be

followed up in studies on larger samples of the population. So far this is the only study in Norway that tells us anything about life-time prevalence in adult women. The results support the assumption that rape is more common than the police figures reflect, even in Norway.

1.2.2.2. The Impact of Rape on the Psychosocial Functioning of the Victim

The relationship between mental health problems and rape was first studied in Scandinavia by the Danish forensic psychiatrist Emma Vestergård, who examined 12 women who had been victims of rape 18 months to 13 years previously. They had all reported the crime to the police. Vestergård concluded that they had all suffered serious acute shock reactions, that four had developed severe neuroses afterwards and that nearly all the women still had anxiety problems such as fear of the dark and being alone (Vestergård, 1974).

Many studies on the impact of rape on victims have, like Emma Vestergård's, been restrospective (Cohen and Roth, 1987; Meyer and Taylor, 1986; Santiago et al., 1985; Girelli et al, 1986). The samples in these studies are mainly drawn from counselling or treatment agencies, sometimes also from advertisements in newspapers. These studies mainly give a picture of the reactions/symptoms that some women have who seek therapeutic assistance or answer advertisements. When such reactions/symptoms are similar to those found in prospective studies, they may have a confirmative value. They can also confirm that long-term symptoms exist, but not how common they are. The retrospective studies may also identify problems that occur after some years, the delayed effects developing in victims who avoided contact with helpers and police in the early phase or who dropped out quickly. However, the results are more difficult to evaluate and make generalizations from.

For the study of mental health problems after rape, prospective follow-up studies constitute the main interest. These studies are also most relevant as a background for the present study. In the following, a presentation of some of the major follow-up studies in the field will be given.

The Burgess and Holmstrom study. The researchers, a psychiatric nurse and a sociologist, were contacted by the nursing staff at

Boston City Hospital each time a rape victim was admitted over a one-year period. Thus their participation rate was 100 percent. Their interview was unstructured: certain topics were to be discussed with each victim, but the questions were open-ended and conducted in a flexible way. The follow-up was done usually by telephone (home visits were also used) several times in the first three months, then at six months, nine months, one year and four to six years after the assault. The average number of follow-up interviews with the victims was five (Holmstrom and Burgess, 1983). At one year and four–six years they had personal contact by either telephone or home visit with 85 percent of the victims (Burgess and Holmstrom, 1979). The reaction to rape was described as a two-phase crisis reaction: an acute disorganization phase and a long-term reorganization phase, called "the Rape Trauma Syndrome" (Burgess and Holmstrom, 1974). The acute reaction was described as dominated by physical symptoms and disorganization in the woman's lifestyle. Fear was the most prominent emotional reaction. The long-term reorganization phase was characterized by nightmares, traumatophobia and what they described as increased motor activity. The study also reported changes in sexual activity and sexual response; a majority reported changes in sexual activity after the rape and many of the sexually active victims reported aversive reactions to sex, half of them had flashbacks and about one-quarter reported pain or discomfort (Burgess and Holmstrom, 1979).

The study has methodological weaknesses regarding its assessment procedures. As an explorative study, however, it has been of great importance in its description of post-rape emotional problems and for stimulating further research.

The Beth Israel follow-up study. This study has a participation rate of 47 percent after the exclusion of 42 out of 130 raped women who contacted a general hospital emergency room during a 12-month period. The follow-up took place 15–30 months later. The interview included open-ended questions about life-changes as well as specific questions about symptoms. The most frequent symptoms at the time of the follow-up were: suspicion of others, fear of going out, sexual difficulties, fear of being alone, and depression. The study also provides information on positive changes in the wake of a traumatic experience, defined as maturation and growth. This study was conducted by experienced clinicians and provides valuable information, especially about the post-traumatic stress nature of the symptoms and the importance of sexual dysfunctions. However, it lacks the use of standardized measurements, it is selective in follow-up procedure, and had a high drop-out ratio (Nadelson et al., 1982).

Other longitudinal studies. Three major cooperating projects – the Atlanta study, the Charleston study and the Pittsburg study – examined the effects of sexual assault on the victim's psychological and interpersonal functioning and were similar in research design (Resick et al., 1981; Calhoun et al., 1982; Atkeson et al., 1982, Kilpatrick et al., 1979, Kilpatrick et al., 1981; Kilpatrick, 1985; Frank and Stewart, 1984; Ellis, 1983).

All three co-operating studies exhibited reliable assessment procedures and repeated assessments the first year after the assault. One study also included a follow-up at two years, three years and four years after the rape (Kilpatrick, 1985). The major problem in these studies is the low participation rate and the high drop-out ratio. A participation rate of 12–45 percent seems to be the case for some studies (Calhoun et al., 1982; Kilpatrick et al., 1981). Sometimes the real participation rate is not mentioned at all; the researchers state only how many actually participated out of those who agreeed to be contacted, not how many were asked. They then report a participation rate of 50–62 percent (Frank and Stewart, 1984; Kilpatrick, 1985). The drop-out ratio seems to be high and sometimes also difficult to evaluate. For example in the Charleston study, 12 (6 percent) out of 204 victims assessed in the acute stage completed the three-year assessment. However, some victims who completed a successful treatment programme were excluded (Kilpatrick, 1985). In the Atlanta study, 31 percent completed six assessments the first 12 months; in the Pittsburg study, 36 percent completed the one-year assessment.

The link to the original emergency room victim is weak. Although it is emphasized that research participants do not differ from non-participants in demographic or rape situation variables, their psychological status may be very different. All of these studies used comparison groups matched for age, race and socioeconomic status. Ellis notes that, at least in the Atlanta study, the victims and controls were different in pre-rape functioning and shows how difficult it might be to find a matching comparison group (Ellis, 1983). Although the victim/comparison group studies have weaknesses, the comparison between victims and non-victims has given a better understanding of specific rape-related symptoms and supported the hypothesis that rape has an impact on mental health.

A major finding in all three studies was that the intensity of the problems changes around three to four months after the rape and after that the change was relatively small. Whereas depressive reactions and social adjustment problems returned to normal after the first three to four months, anxiety and phobic reactions were the most specific long-lasting problems. This coincides with the early explorative studies which found that trauma-related fears were common long-lasting problems.

Taking all the prospective studies together, the conclusion is that they mutually support the hypothesis that rape has an impact on mental health.

Post-Traumatic Stress Disorder (PTSD). The introduction of the diagnosis "Post-Traumatic Stress Disorder" in the American Psychiatric Association's *Diagnostic and Statistical Manual* in 1980 (DSM-III, 1980) was the consequence of growing knowledge about the consistency of the human response to overwhelming and uncontrollable life-events. The responses had been described earlier as traumatic neurosis (Kardiner, 1941), and later as the stress-response syndrome (Horowitz, 1976). The essential feature of the disorder is the development of characteristic symptoms following a psychologically distressing event that is outside the range of usual human experience and that would be markedly distressing to almost anyone, e.g. a serious threat to one's life or physical integrity, a serious threat to a close person or watching another person be seriously injured or killed. The characteristic symptoms involve re-experiencing the traumatic event, avoidance of stimuli associated with the event or numbing of general responsiveness, and signs of increased arousal such as hypervigilance, exaggerated startle response, irritability, difficulties in concentrating, sleep disturbances and physiological reactivity upon exposure to an event that symbolizes or resembles the traumatic event (DSM-III, 1980). For further details of the diagnostic criteria see Chapter 2. The post-traumatic stress response has been described as phasic, with periods of re-experiencing and hyperarousal alternating with periods of numbing, emotional constriction, social isolation and avoidance (van der Kolk, 1987).

After the introduction of PTSD in DSM-III, Burgess and Holstrom argued that the symptoms they had found in victims of rape fitted the diagnostic criteria for PTSD (Burgess and Holmstrom, 1985). Nadelson and co-workers wrote that, although crisis theory provides a useful framework for understanding the dynamics of the short-term effects of rape, its applicability to long-term effects can be questioned. They suggested PTSD as an alternative conceptualization (Nadelson et al., 1982). Kilpatrick et al. (1979) described the reaction to rape as a classical conditioned response to a life-threatening situation. These authors later compared the diagnostic criteria for PTSD with the symptoms most commonly experienced by rape victims and suggested that rape produces PTSD in many victims (Kilpatrick et al., 1985). The earlier follow-up studies indicate that post-traumatic stress symptoms exist in rape victims after the assault. To meet the diagnostic criteria for the disorder, all diagnostic criteria as well as intensity and frequency of symptoms have to be taken into account. This calls for further investigation of post-traumatic stress symptoms and the development of PTSD as a consequence of rape, as well as looking for specific rape related features in follow-up studies.

1.2.3. FROM IDEA TO PROJECT: THE OEW CONTEXT

The description of the decision-making process in the preparation of the admission service for sexual assault victims and the service itself is included in this monograph for two reasons.

First, involving and preparing the staff for the service were considered part of the project. Without the service, getting in contact with victims of rape and finding out how they could best be helped by the health service would be more difficult. It was of primary interest to get into contact with victims who approached the health service. The staff were considered to be crucial in the establishment of contact, since they had to distribute the information about the study to the patients. I assumed that if they knew me, and I worked with them instead of arriving as a stranger requiring their cooperation, the chances of getting into contact with the victims would be better.

Second, by describing the service itself, and how people were informed about it, my intention has been to describe the sample-source from which my sample was chosen. It also describes the context in which I worked and what procedure the participants in my study had been through before I saw them.

1.2.3.1. The Context of the Research Project: the First Phase of the Admission Service for Rape Victims

In 1985 I was asked to join a commission appointed by the Chief Medical Officer in Oslo to draw up a plan of action for a medical service for rape victims. The plan proposed that a rape admission service for the city of Oslo should be situated at the municipal Oslo Emergency Ward (OEW). When the plan was accepted and I received a grant for a research project, I was convinced that it was imperative to become familiar with the personnel and work routines of the Emergency Ward. Likewise, it was essential for them to get to know me as a professional, so that they could present the study in a manner which encouraged the participation of the patients. I therefore approached the preliminary work at the ward as part of the preparation for the project.

In connection with the approval of the plan of action by the Oslo Board of Health, a resolution was made regarding two preparatory procedures:

(1) The appointment of a Professional Panel at Oslo Emergency Ward (OEW) that would be responsible for carrying through the plan of action. The Commissioner of Health gave me the task of appointing the panel and serving as its acting chairman during the initial period. Representatives of the affected wards at OEW – the general health section, the psychiatric and social emergency service sections – were elected to the panel. In addition, a representative was elected from the secondary health services: a psychologist from Tøyen Psychiatric Out-patient Clinic who was working on developing methods for the treatment of battered and raped women.

(2) The engagement of a medical consultant as coordinator for the admissions centre. Dr Lisbeth Bang was asked to accept this position. Her task at OEW was initially to prepare a medical and forensic journal in collaboration with the general health section. She was responsible for contacts and collaboration with the Institute of Forensic Medicine and the police. She also planned and carried through a training and teaching pro-gramme for all concerned parties at OEW.

My own duties, besides leading the Professional Panel, were to prepare the psychosocial part of the admission service and to establish a counselling journal. Furthermore, I took part in plan-ning the teaching programme and was responsible for educating the staff on the themes of crises, trauma reactions and crisis inter-vention with special attention to the reactions of victims of sexual assault.

Prior to the opening of the admissions service on 8 January 1986, every staff member – from the security guard to the nurses, doctors and social workers – had undergone the teaching programme. The Professional Panel had worked together for five months and had approved all aspects of the service. The public was well informed of the service through newspapers, radio and TV. Informative pamphlets were displayed at pharmacies, social security and physicians' offices and at police stations. The Institute of Forensic Medicine had sanctioned the arrangements for the forensic examination, and the police agreed to cooperate. The arrangement was that everyone who contacted the police regarding rape in Oslo would be brought to OEW for examination and offered the services as planned. OEW would also admit rape victims who made direct contact without having gone via the police. The shelter for raped and battered women was also specially informed about our service.

Age of target group. Questions were raised at an early stage in the Professional Panel regarding the need for a special service for children. The staff were quick to point out that medical examinations and taking care of children would require paediatric competence, and that OEW perhaps was not the right place for examinations of this type. The coordinator of the admissions service therefore contacted the paediatric departments at Ullevål and Aker hospitals to involve them in finding a solution to this question. By the time the service opened, an age limit of 14 years had been set for admission to OEW. The Department of Paediatrics at Aker Hospital volunteered to admit and examine children who had been sexually assaulted in Oslo, but all the preparations and agreements had not been made in time for the opening of the centre at OEW. Children under 14 years of age were therefore admitted during the first few months of operation.

1.2.3.2. Rape Victim Services at OEW: Second Phase

The facility at OEW was integrated with already existing services. A prerequisite for this decision was that rape victims, who had previously been neglected and poorly treated by the health authorities, would now receive better treatment. This could be achieved by carefully planned procedures for admission and treatment of the patient group as well as by educating the staff. Concretely stated, the services provided were as follows:

1. The medical service. This involved:
    offer of a forensic examination with collection of evidence;

offer to store all evidence and test results at OEW for four weeks if the patient was undecided about whether she/he would prosecute the assailant;

offer of medical care and check-ups, including those patients not interested in a forensic examination. This covered examination of wounds, possible infection by venereal diseases, and HIV virus, and pregnancy tests with follow-up checks after two and eight weeks.

Responsibility for this part of the service was held by the general health section at OEW, dubbed "the corridor". Nurses belonging to this section acted as coordinators of admissions, i.e. when an assault victim was identified at any place in the Emergency Ward system, notice was given to the on-duty nurse at the general health section who would then meet and bring the patient to a room reserved for this type of admission. There, the nurse would try to assess the situation and needs of the patient, inform about the services available, introduce a counsellor and make a decision about what step should be taken next. In principle, the medical examination should be undertaken as quickly as possible. Whether this was feasible depended both on the situation in "the corridor" and on the patient's need to calm down and their fear or doubt regarding their wish to undergo the examination in question.

2. *The psychosocial service.* Psychosocial counselling was presented as an opportunity to talk about the emotional aspects of the injury and the immediate interpersonal and practical concerns and consequences. This also included working with and possibly caring for family members or others who had accompanied the patient. The counselling service also had the responsibility, in cooperation with the patient and next of kin, to plan what was to happen after the examination, to discuss the need for provision of a safe place to stay, and to make contact with an attorney and the police. The counselling service also supplied information about the possibilities for further assistance by secondary health services, and took responsibility for following up the patient during the next few days until a further course of action had been decided upon.

During the first year of operation, the counselling service established a network of contacts at psychiatric outpatient clinics and family counselling centres to ensure that referrals would go smoothly. The counselling part of the service was initially conducted by psychiatric nurses of the psychiatric emergency service or by the social emergency service. These decided among themselves who should have day-to-day responsibility. In the psychiatric emergency service, four nurses shared duties from 4 p.m. to 8 a.m. and were a relatively stable group. The on-duty psychiatrists made up a much larger group and were infrequently on call within shorter time periods; they were therefore a poorer base from which to establish stable cooperation. The social emergency service had 24-hour operations and a steady staff, so the majority of counselling tasks were awarded to them.

3. *Temporary accommodation service.* This offered a 24-hour stay in OEW's observation ward when there was a need for care and safe accommodation until an alternative could be arranged. The observation ward was a clinical bed ward that served all the emergency services at OEW. At that time, the ward was geographically close to the reception room for sexually assaulted patients and to the psychiatric and social emergency services.

When the service opened, it became clear that people who had been sexually assaulted contacted the Emergency Ward in different ways:

– they were brought to OEW by the police, who applied for a medico-legal examination;
– they were accompanied to OEW by rape shelter personnel, who asked for medical examinations or other help provided by OEW;
– they were accompanied to OEW by concerned network persons: friends, lovers, family members, neighbours, colleagues, teachers or other persons in whom they had confided;
– they contacted OEW themselves and asked for help.

In the last two instances, the victims had received information about our services by way of radio, the press, TV, pamphlets or from acquaintances. The public information that had been spread asked people to phone first for details about what to say when they arrived at the Emergency Ward. Upon arrival at reception, it was necessary that they communicated in some manner that they were in need of urgent attention. Most of the victims were accompanied by someone who helped them to convey this message. We suggested that people should say to the receptionist that they had contacted us because of S.A. (abbreviation for sexual assault). The personnel at OEW were instructed to take seriously anyone who said they had come because of sexual assault, and to admit and examine them on the basis of these premises.

In some cases, however, it was impossible to discover what had happened owing to the patient being confused, psychotic or severely intoxicated. If it was possible to get a patient to accept a stay in the observation ward, this was done to attempt to clarify the circumstances. However, if the message about sexual assault was not clarified or confirmed by examination of the victim, the case was not registered.

With the opening of the services, the direct work with the present study also started. The victims could now be approached to volunteer for the study.

2

Problem Approach in this Study

2.1. Rape and Health – What Remains to be Investigated?

Research on the psychosocial consequences of rape for the victim has been going on for the last 20 years. The main studies and results have been presented in Chapter 1.

Although most studies of short- and long-term psychological reactions have weaknesses, the repeated documentation of post-rape psychological reactions, in both retrospective and longitudinal studies, with or without comparison groups, should be sufficient for it to be accepted that rape-related mental health problems exist. For clinical purposes, however there is a need for further psychiatric documentation of the nature and severity of the problems in a prospective study with a satisfactory follow-up rate. The long-term reactions to rape have not been fully investigated in a spectrum from mild reactions to clinical disorders. The presence of Post-Traumatic Stress Disorder as well as co-morbidity with other rape-related disorders should be more fully explored, as this is important for the choice of treatment strategy.

The trauma of rape itself has received little attention in research on reactions to rape. To explore the traumatic event and how it is experienced and interpreted by the victim might be of importance for understanding the psychological response to rape, difficulties in coping as well as the nature of long-term problems. A better understanding of what the victim has been through could be of crucial importance to clinical treatment. Whereas the main focus in the victim/comparison group studies has been to compare victims with non-victims, relatively little is known about variations and differences within the victim group regarding the course of the reaction and the nature of long-term psychological problems.

To look for predictors, identified in the acute phase, which can be used by emergency care services for detecting victims at risk could contribute to better prevention and earlier treatment. The search for predictors has not been done in any systematic way in longitudinal studies. The main focus in the longitudinal studies has been the psychosocial consequences and not health problems in general.

From a medical point of view there is a need for an exploration of somatic health complaints along with the mental health problems. These considerations led to the following research questions for the present study:

1 (a) Is rape an event outside the range of normal human experience as defined in the A criterion of PTSD (DSM-III-R, 1987 – see definition later in this chapter)? How can the event be described and analysed when the aim is to understand its psychological impact?
    (b) Which elements of the rape experience are identified and recognized as particularly stressful by the victims?
    (c) Are there similarities and differences in the pattern of the rape experiences which makes it reasonable to categorize rape into different types?

2 (a) Is the nature of the immediate psychological response to rape a general crisis reaction or can it be characterized as a specific post-traumatic stress reaction with the features of PTSD?
    (b) Does the acute response to rape have specific rape-related features of importance for clinical practice?

3 (a) How does the psychological response to rape change in the course of the first year?
    (b) Do all victims follow the same pattern or are there variations within the victim group?

4 (a) What are the long-term mental health consequences of rape?
    (b) Do victims of rape display long-term post-traumatic stress symptoms and/or the full Post-Traumatic Stress Disorder (PTSD)? If so, what is the co-morbidity with other rape-related disorders?

5 (a) Is it possible to identify factors in the acute phase which predict a risk for developing long-term mental health problems?
    (b) Are there specific predictors for PTSD and other rape-related disorders?

6 (a) Does the rape experience influence or change the victim's perception of and relationship to self and others? If so, are these changes related to a psychiatric disorder outcome?

7 (a) What do the victims do to cope with their reaction? What are the main differences in coping within the group and how are these related to psychiatric outcome?

8 (a) What are the immediate somatic health consequences after rape?

(b) Are there any changes in reported somatic health the year before and after rape? If so, how are these changes related to the psychiatric consequences?

(c) What is the nature of the somatic health complaints after the assault?

2.2. Definitions and Concepts

2.2.1. RAPE

Rape is defined both as forced sexual intercourse and as taking anything by force - "to force or violate" (Longman New Universal Dictionary, 1982).

2.2.1.1. The law

In the Norwegian legal system, rape has been forbidden by law for the last thousand years, as long as we have knowledge of a written law in Norway (Gulatingsloven). Until 1687 rape was listed among the violent crimes; in this year, owing to the influence of the church, rape was listed under a new chapter concerning immorality. The law was also amended by categorizing victims into honourable (honest maids and widows) and more doubtful females (Lykkjen, 1976).

In the present law of 1902 (revised in 1927, 1963 and 1981), the law on sexual offences is also placed under crimes against moral conduct, chapter 19 (Norges Lover, 1983). The present law is gender neutral, in relation to both offender and victim.

A person who by violence or by inducing fear for anybody's life or health forces someone to unlawful sexual relations or assists in such, should be punished for rape with up to 10 years' imprisonment, but with at least one year if the unlawful sexual relation was intercourse. (Paragraph 192)

Thus penetration is not seen as a condition for rape in the present Norwegian law. Paragraph 193 discusses unlawful sexual relations with an unconscious person, or someone who for other reasons, e.g. physical illness, cannot offer resistance. To take advantage of someone's mental illness or mental retardation is also included in this paragraph. Paragraph 194 discusses unlawful sexual relations attained by threats, cunning behaviour or abuse of dependency. Paragraphs 193 and 194 are not, however, seen as rape legally. Thus the Norwegian law is on the one hand narrow in its definition of rape, by its sole emphasis on the use of force, and on the other hand broad in not demanding penetration and in being gender natural. Paragraph 195 deals with unlawful sexual relations with children under the age of 16.

Nadelson and co-workers write that in the United States most statutes define rape as carnal knowledge of a person against the will of the person. Two elements are necessary to constitute the crime: (i) sexual intercourse and (ii) failure to seek or obtain the consent of the victim (Nadelson, Notman and Carmen, 1986).

In England and Wales, Section 1 of the Sexual Offences (Amendment) Act 1976 provides that a man commits rape if (a) he has unlawful sexual intercourse with a woman who at the time of the intercourse does not consent to it, and (b) at that time, he knows she does not consent to the intercourse or is reckless as to whether she consents to it (Blair, 1985).

This last point is included in the Norwegian law through the conditions for punishment, namely the subjective conditions of guilt linked to intent (Andenæs and Bratholm, 1990). The offender can escape punishment if he is unaware of acting against the will of the victim. If he admits that she said no, but that he did not think she meant it seriously, it is difficult to prove his malicious intent unless he has injured her, or there are witnesses to the crime. In addition to this, the general rule is that the accused should benefit from any doubt concerning his/her guilt. Thus the credibility of the victim may become a main issue.

Both American and English law put more emphasis on the non-consent of the victim than the Norwegian law does in its text.

2.2.1.2. Definition of Rape in the Present Study

In a study where the main focus is the impact of the event on the victim, the understanding of the event will necessarily be different from a description of the event, where the main focus is on the actions of the offender. In the present study, rape is defined as

> penetration (vaginal, anal or oral) carried out without consent by force, threat of force, or use of power in a situation where the victim is not in a condition to give consent. Attempted rape is defined as attempted sexual intercourse without consent where no penetration has taken place.

For the victim, the main point is that attempted or actual sexual penetration is *forced upon her without regard to her will* by inducing fear or by attacking her in a defenceless vulnerable position where she has no chance of opposing, such as when she is drugged or asleep.

The definition used here differs from the Norwegian legal definition in making a distinction between attempted and completed rape (a stricter definition) as well as in including sexual assault in situations where the victim is not able to give consent (a broader definition). This is done because this is more in accord with the studies from USA, where they make this distinction. The distinction is also made because my impression from clinical practice is that penetration is an important issue for the victim. Further, from the victim's point of view, the main issue is that the sexual contact is forced upon her against her will, whether this is by taking advantage of a situation in which she cannot give consent, or by the use of threats, force or violence.

2.2.2. THE DIAGNOSTIC CRITERIA FOR PTSD

Since the development of Post-Traumatic Stress Disorder (PTSD) will be of main interest in the present study, the diagnostic criteria from DSM-III-R (1987) will be listed here.

A. The person has experienced an event that is outside the range of normal human experience and that would be markedly distressing to almost anyone, e.g. serious threat to one's life or physical integrity; serious threat or harm to one's children, spouse or other close relatives and friends; sudden destruction of one's home or community; or seeing another person who has recently been, or is being, seriously injured or killed as the result of an accident or physical violence.

B. The traumatic event is persistently re-experienced in at least one of the following ways:
   (1) recurrent and intrusive distressing recollections of the event (in young children repetitive play in which themes or aspects of the trauma are expressed)
   (2) recurrent distressing dreams of the event
   (3) sudden acting or feeling as if the traumatic event were recurring (includes a sense of reliving the experience, illusions, hallucinations and dissociative (flashbacks) episodes, even those that occur upon awakening or when intoxicated
   (4) intense psychological distress at exposure to events that symbolize or resemble an aspect of the traumatic event, including anniversaries of the trauma

C. Persistent avoidance of stimuli associated with the trauma or numbing of general responsiveness (not present before the trauma), as indicated by at least three of the following:
   (1) efforts to avoid thoughts or feelings associated with the trauma
   (2) efforts to avoid activities or situations that arouse recollections of the trauma
   (3) inability to recall important aspects of the trauma (psychogenic amnesia)
   (4) markedly diminished interest in significant activities (in young children loss of recently acquired developmental skills such as toilet training or language skills)
   (5) feelings of detachment or estrangement from others
   (6) restricted range of affect, e.g. unable to have loving feelings
   (7) sense of a foreshortened future, e.g. does not expect to have a career, children or a long life
D. Persistent symptoms of increased arousal (not present before the trauma) as indicated by at least two of the following:
   (1) difficulty falling or staying asleep
   (2) irritability or outbursts of anger
   (3) difficulty concentrating
   (4) hypervigilance
   (5) exaggerated startle response
   (6) physiological reactivity upon exposure to events that symbolize or resemble an aspect of the traumatic event (e.g. a woman who was raped in an elevator breaks out in a sweat when entering any elevator)
E. Duration of the disturbance (symptoms in B, C and D) of at least one month.

2.3. Conclusion

Views on what remains to be investigated regarding rape and consequences for health are dictated by a clinical perspective: which questions still need to be answered so that victims of rape who seek assistance in the health service may get useful help? Identifying the nature of a stressor, of health problems and of predictors is of interest because within the health system it leads to better treatment. Two important concepts and definitions – rape and PTSD – are presented as a necessary background to both methodology and results.

3

Materials and Methods

This chapter will describe the design, the participants and the data collection in the present study. Later, in relation to the presentation of the results, the methods that are relevant to that particular part of the study will be summarized and when necessary explained in more detail.

3.1. Design

The design chosen for the study is that of a longitudinal cohort study. No comparison group was selected (for discussion of this see Chapter 11), thus only a within-group design was applied. The assessments started with a personal semi-structured interview and standardized questionnaires within two weeks of exposure to a rape, followed by the same standardized questionnaires after three months and a personal semi-structured interview and the same questionnaires again after one year (13–16 months). The timing of the assessments followed recommendations from colleagues doing research in disaster psychiatry (see Raphael et al., 1989). The personal interviews were all done by the author.

3.2. The Data Collection

3.2.1. ESTABLISHING CONTACT

Everyone who agreed to participate in the study was contacted by the researcher as soon as possible after admission. The researcher was present at the Emergency Ward every day. Sometimes it was possible to make contact with the victim during admission; 15 victims were contacted in this way. The others were reached by telephone or letter. It was not always possible to fix a time for the first assessment at once. The participants often had several difficult problems to deal with in the first few days, such as getting in touch with an assistant lawyer and giving further statements to the police. When this was the case, the first agreement concerned how to keep in touch until the first assessment could take place. In all cases much emphasis was put on getting in touch with the participants as soon as possible, as it was assumed that this would increase the possibility of participation.

3.2.2. THE COLLECTION OF DATA

3.2.2.1. Standardized Instruments Used in all Three Assessments – the Self-rating Scales

Four self-rating scales were chosen. They were administered before the interview. The self-rating scales had been used in other studies of traumatized populations, thus the possibility for later comparison of results was open. It was also a consideration that the participants should find the questionnaires relevant and understand that they were related to their actual situation. Another consideration was that the questionnaires should not have too many questions in case the participants had concentration difficulties and felt restless. The four self-rating scales were:

1. *The Impact of Event Scale* (IES), created by Horowitz and coworkers, measures the intensity of intrusive and avoidance symptoms related to the traumatic event (Horowitz et al., 1979; Horowitz, 1982). The scale has 15 items, a scoring range for each item of 0–5 and includes two subscales, one for intrusion (range 0–35) and one for avoidance (range 0–40) with definitions of low (0–8), medium (9–19) and high (20–) levels of distress on both subscales. The intrusion subscale measures the intensity of involuntary re-experiences of the trauma. The avoidance subscale yields a measure of how strongly the person tries to avoid being reminded of the trauma. The scale is designed to record the presence and intensity of specific post-traumatic stress symptoms and is widely recognised and used in traumatic stress research, including in Norway (Malt, 1988; Weisæth, 1989; Holen, 1990).
2. *The Speilberger State Anxiety Inventory* (Spielberger, 1970). A 12-item version was used (STAI x-1). This version includes 10 items from the original 20-item version (items 1, 2, 3, 5, 7, 11, 12, 13, 14) and two items from the Spielberger State Personality Inventory (items 25 and 28; Spielberger, 1970). The scoring range for each item was 1–4 and for the whole test 12–48. The scale has also been used in a Norwegian study of physically injured adults and its validity has been tested (Malt and Olafsen, 1992).

Six questions on state aggression (here labelled STAGI) from Spielberger's State Personality Inventory were added to the State Anxiety scale (items 3, 9, 12, 15, 18 and 21). The possible range of this scale was 6–24 (Spielberger, 1979).

3. *A stress-symptom list* (SSL) created by Leyman (1985) for victims of violent crimes was chosen mainly because it included psychophysiological reactions. The list was shortened and 20 items mainly describing psychophysiological stress symptoms were picked out: headache, backache, muscle-ache, dizziness, difficulties with memory, difficulties concentrating, difficulties falling asleep, interrupted sleep, nightmares, early awakening, stomach-ache, diarrhoea, constipation, nausea, vomiting, reduced appetite, trembling, attacks of sweating, palpitations, difficulties breathing. In the first assessment the SSL recorded the reactions in the first week after the assault including the present state, whereas the later assessments recorded the preceding four weeks on a 0–3 score.

4. *General Health Questionnaire* (GHQ; Goldberg and Williams, 1988). A 20-item version was chosen (GHQ-20). This version had also been used in other traumatic stress studies in Norway (Malt, 1989; Holen, 1990). The 0–0–1–1 scoring version was chosen in the present study. At the first assessment the participants were asked to fill out the GHQ-20 questionnaire for the two weeks prior to the assault. For the second and third assessments it was filled out for the two weeks preceding the assessments.

The validity and reliability of the self-assessment instruments STAI x-1, IES and GHQ-20 have been documented in earlier studies (Malt, 1988, 1989; Malt and Olafsen, 1992).

In addition, information on coping was collected at all three assessments. No standardized measurements on coping were chosen. The participants were asked to describe in their own words their efforts to deal with what had happened and their responses to it. At the three-month assessment this information could be given by letter. The statements were categorized later. For further details see Chapter 9.

3.2.2.2. *Standardized Instruments and Questions Included in the Two Interviews – in the Acute Stage and After a Year*

The Comprehensive Psychopathological Rating Scale (CPRS) developed by Åsberg et al. (1978) has its own interview manual with criteria for each score. A seven-point ordinal scoring procedure was used. Malt added 11 items to the original 28 basic non-psychotic symptoms in order to cover all symptoms needed for the diagnosis of anxiety disorders and Post-Traumatic Stress Disorder (CPRS – PTSD; Malt, 1988). In addition, shame was included as an item. For this item, the definition and criteria followed the pattern of description of the other symptoms. All symptoms were coded with reference to the present state. In the first assessment a score for the previous six months was given. The symptoms were scored 0–6, where 0–1 (0) meant absent or minimally present, 2–3 (1) moderately present, 4–5 (2) present in such a degree that they influence the person's ability to function, and 6 (3) indicating no control over the symptom at all.

Example: Shame related to the rape experience.
Definition: Feelings of shame indicated by a wish to keep the experience hidden from others because it creates distress that others know what has happened. 0–1: none or very slight feelings of shame in connection with what has happened; 2–3: often a distressing feeling of shame, distressed by the thought that others know, a wish to keep it hidden from others, but the feeling is influenced by the situation and can be forgotten in between. 4–5: continuous feeling of shame and a strong wish to keep the experience hidden from others. Feeling that other people might know about the rape just by looking at the victim. Problems with going out and meeting other people because of this, but manages to get absolutely essential things done; 6: strong continuous feeling of shame. Thinks everybody can see what has happened. Does not go out, avoids other people and doesn't get necessary things (like shopping for food) done because of the shame feeling.

The sum-scores were made on the basis of the CPRS–PTSD scores. These were the subscale for depression created by Montgomery and Åsberg (MADRS) of 10 items (Montgomery et al., 1986). In addition a scale of 10 post-traumatic stress (PTS) items consistent with 10 DSM-III-R criteria for Post-Traumatic Stress Disorder was created. The items were: involuntary re-experiencing (thoughts, images, flashbacks); nightmares; loss of interest; withdrawal; trauma-avoidance (phobic avoidance of trauma-related places, themes, actions); reduced sleep; irritability; difficulties concentrating; hypervigilance; exaggerated startle response.

Somatic health – repeated questions. Contact with physicians during the previous year according to the number of consultations and reasons for contact were noted. The participants were also asked to give a judgement about whether their somatic health had been as usual, worse than usual or better than usual during the previous year. Specific complaints as reasons for worse health were noted.

Social network and social support. In mapping the participants' social network, a social network diagram which the participants filled out themselves was administered. The diagram maps important relations, and indicates closeness and distance (Antonucci and Depner, 1982).

Social support was measured on an eight-question questionnaire with five different possible scores (Sørensen, 1991). Both instruments have been used in Norwegian studies concerning mental health, social networks and social support.

Satisfaction in partner relationship. Two visual analogue scales of 0–10 were used for measuring satisfaction in existing partner relationship at the time, one for general satisfaction and one for sexual satisfaction.

Sexual satisfaction. Satisfaction with sexual life over the previous year was asked to be evaluated by the participants as mainly very positive, positive, indifferent, negative or very negative. Specific problems were then explored.

3.2.2.3. The Interviews

Both interviews were semi-structured. Although the majority of questions had categories for answers, personal answers which did not fit the categories were written down and a final coding of categorization took place before the information was punched. When qualitative clinical interview data were quantified into ordinal scales (e.g. same as before, worse than before, better than before or not at all, a little, moderately, considerably) this had been worked out beforehand and the interviewer checked with the participant whether the answer was understood correctly.

The first interview. This was conducted within two weeks of the assault; the median day for this first interview was the fifth day (range 2nd–14th day). It lasted mostly from 3–5 hours divided between 1–3 sessions. In only four cases was the first assessment completed in one session.

The aim of the interview was to collect information about the person involved, including her network, the traumatic experience, the immediate reaction, coping and the present state. In addition to the measurements and questions repeated in the second or third assessment (see above), specific information collected in the first interview was:

(1) *Sociodemographic data* (see section 3.3.1 below).
(2) *Information about the rape event.* A detailed description of the traumatic event was elicited by a thorough interview about what had happened, the offender's behaviour and the victim's thoughts, feelings and actions, before, during and immediately afterwards. (For further details see Chapter 4). Every victim was asked for permission to tape this part of the interview. In 33 cases such permission was granted on condition that nobody else except the interviewer should listen to the tape. When the story was not taped, it was written down directly in the interview situation; when taped, it was written down afterwards from the tape-recording.
(3) *The immediate reactions of the victim after the event,* including thoughts, feelings, bodily reactions and behaviour. This included information about how long it took before others were contacted, who was contacted and the immediate reactions from important others, including police, women's refuge centre/shelter, and health personnel.
(4) *Background and earlier life.* This part was divided into:
   (a) *Family background and childhood environment.* The interviewing about family relations and childhood environment was a continuation of the interview about social network. The interviewer drew a genogram (McGoldrick and Gerson, 1985) and used this for further investigations of family relations at the present time and how the relations had been before. Primary care persons during childhood, losses through death or divorce, parental health, problems with abuse, and violence between parents were noted specifically. Based on this information, the researcher also made a global assessment about whether the atmosphere in childhood had been "good", "usual" or "poor". "Atmosphere in childhood" was scored "good" when what was communicated about atmosphere and relations indicated clearly

positive elements, such as warm, supportive, stable and trusting relationships. "Usual" was scored when nothing specially negative (like violence, alcohol abuse, neglect) or clearly positive (warm, supportive, stable and trusting) was communicated about the conditions in the family of origin. "Poor" was scored for specifically negative conditions and relationships like violence, alcohol abuse, physical or sexual abuse or abandonment of parental care.

(b) *Earlier life-events*. The participants were asked about life-events they had found difficult to cope with, and were also asked specifically about life-events such as births, deaths, abortions, serious illnesses affecting close network persons, separation or divorce, loss of job in the year before the rape.

(c) *Earlier health*. This was divided into somatic health and mental health. Serious, longlasting or repeated somatic health problems were asked for, including investigation of hospital treatment.

The investigation of mental health included questions about nervous symptoms, professional treatment including hospital treatment, use of psychotropic drugs and whether nervous or psychiatric symptoms had ever inhibited their ability to function adequately.

(d) Use and abuse of *alcohol and drugs* were investigated by questions about the frequency and amount of use. Contact with treatment institutions for abuse problems was noted.

(e) Earlier *experience with sexual assault and violence*. The participants were asked about unpleasant or forced sexual encounters with grown-ups during childhood and adolescence, and earlier rape experiences. Experiences of childhood physical punishment and physical abuse as well as physical abuse later in life were also recorded.

The interview situation. The first interviews took place in a small dreary office on the gound floor of the old building of the Emergency Ward, with the accompanying sound of roaring traffic outside its windows. The participants were often restless and upset and had difficulties with concentration from time to time. They all had their own specific traumatic experience, it took time to reveal it, and sometimes it was done with great difficulty. The interview also included many other intimate questions, which sometimes increased the distress. Earlier difficult experiences never spoken of before were revealed. It was necessary to explain why the questions were asked and the purpose of the different procedures: "In order to understand your present situation fully, it helps to know who you were before this happened, how you usually handle difficult situations, if there is anybody you know you can rely on when you have difficulties, etc." It was also necessary to follow the pace of the participant, to take breaks and/or postpone the rest of the interview to the next day. The clinician and the researcher were often in conflict – the clinician thinking, "better wait, take time", while the researcher was anxious to get the information, thinking "maybe you won't get another chance". It was, however, important to be flexible. Some participants were restless and seemed anxious and then it was necessary to take time, to ask about what bothered them, if there was something in the interview situation that worried them, and so on. Others could seem quite unemotional and calm at the beginning of the interview, sometimes explaining that what had happened did not seem real at all, it did not bother them. Then, during the detailed interviewing about the traumatic experience, when they also had to recall feelings and thoughts, the situation changed, and sudden feelings of anxiety and aggression towards the interviewer could appear.

Several elements of an assessment can be seen as therapeutic, such as ventilation of feelings and worries, verbalizing and going through the traumatic experience in safe surroundings. However, confirmative support on coping, supportive challenging of negative beliefs and interpretations, discussions of practical solutions, etc. were saved until the assessment was completed.

Effects on the researcher. The intention was that the recruitment of the sample should go on for 12 months. Already after about 20 assessments I started to notice changes in myself. I started to have real nightmares, something I had not had since childhood. I had periods with difficulties falling asleep, I became irritable and unsociable. I started to pester my daughters about possible dangers, and became more vigilant myself. Before the interviews I started to notice a certain resistance in myself against asking about the rape experience. I was surprised by this, regarding myself as a calm, relaxed person, an experienced clinician used to working with people under serious stress and sometimes in extremely difficult life-situations. It helped me when I found out that other researchers had reacted similarly to material on sexual violence. I found it necessary to talk about the interviews to a colleague, and sometimes to my husband who is also a colleague. It helped me to continue, but to overcome the resistance again and again cost me a lot. When I had completed the 55th interview I had reached my limit. I did not want to listen to another assault history! I mention this because I think it is important that researchers in the trauma field communicate this kind of experience to each other. At least it helped me when I found out that others had similar reactions.

The follow-up interview. Forty-seven (89 percent) women were followed up. One declined and five did not reply to my invitation to a follow-up interview. Four of the women who dropped out had participated in the three-month follow-up; three of the drop-outs at the three-month follow-up participated at this last follow-up. That means that 44 women participated in all three assessments. The interview took place at the Emergency Ward or in the home of the participant and lasted 2–3 hours. The aim of the follow-up interview was to identify changes in life-situation, changes in the subjects' mental and physical health, changes in the relationship to self and others which had taken place after the rape and how she felt about the rape in retrospect.

In addition to the repeated measurements and questions (see above) the interview covered the following themes:

(1) Sociodemographic data, changes in life-situation since the first interview.
(2) The reaction. Complaints after the assault, duration of reactions and symptoms, and how these had influenced important areas of functioning such as work, daily activities, social life, love life and sexuality.
(3) In addition to the CPRS–PTSD, the interviewer used the interview protocol SCID (Structured Clinical Interview for DSM-III; Spitzer and Williams, 1984). SCID was used when it was necessary to get information not available on the CPRS such as sexual problems and substance-abuse problems. The SCID interview for PTSD was included in the interview guides. All diagnoses were later revised in accordance with DSM-III-R.
(4) Changes in menstrual cycles, menstrual complaints and pelvic pain in relation to and unrelated to menstruation. These areas were added because the participants started to report such changes spontaneously in my contact with them during the first weeks and at three months.

(5) In addition to the repeated instruments and questions about relationships to others, the participants were interviewed specifically about these changes. They were also interviewed about changes in relation to self (see Chapter 9). This section also included questions concerning if and how other people had been helpful.

(6) Looking back at the rape. This included an open-ended question concerning what she now thinks was worst about the rape experience, as well as specific questions about how she now thinks about the threat of physical harm or death, degradation and humiliation, feeling cheated and helplessness. The content of flashbacks and if there was anything she could not bear to remember (see Chapter 4) were also discussed.

(7) Experience with police and the legal system. Questions in this part of the interview mapped reaction to contact with the police after the acute phase, whether the offender had been identified, whether the case had been prosecuted, should be prosecuted or had been dismissed, and her reactions to this.

After the interview a diagnosis was made according to the *Diagnostic and Statistical Manual of Mental Disorders* (DSM-III-R, 1987). When the criteria for more than one diagnosis were met, a concurrent diagnosis was given additionally. Only new problems that had developed after the rape were diagnosed. If the participants presented symptoms they had reported as pre-rape mental problems at the first assessment (e.g. scored on CPRS–PTSD for the six-month period before the assault or reported specifically when the nature of mental, sexual or substance-abuse problems was explored), these problems were not diagnosed as they were not considered relevant as a consequence of the rape traumatization. These problems were labelled unchanged.

3.2.2.4. Information from Other Sources

Information from other sources than the participants themselves came mainly from the emergency admission, including the recording of physical signs and tests carried out. In 17 cases I also talked to family members who gave additional information about family, former health and their present observation of changes in the participants. In seven cases I talked on the phone to primary care physicians who knew the patients. Concerning the two participants who were in adolescent welfare institutions, I met with the staff of the institutions. The participant who was in a psychiatric aftercare institution allowed me to speak to the psychiatrist who treated her. Information from National Health files for Oslo residents concerning diagnosis in relation to sick leave was also obtained for 24 participants.

3.3. The Participants

3.3.1. THE SAMPLE

During the first 10 months of 1986, 118 persons contacted the new admission service for rape victims at the Oslo Emergency Ward. Recruitment to the research project was done in the following way.

Written information about the research project was handed out during admission at the Emergency Ward. The information included a reply slip to be filled out during the intake. The main rule was that the information should be given by the counsellor (psychiatric nurse or social worker). If the patient did not want any contact with the counsellor, the information should be handed out by the nurse in the general health section. The information also included an offer of therapeutic help, either by the researcher alone or by referral for further help when necessary. It was considered unethical to examine acutely traumatized persons without evaluating their need for help and offering crisis-intervention. However, the possibility of being referred to a psychiatric outpatient clinic or a family counselling clinic was also presented as an alternative for those who did not want to participate in the research project.

3.3.2. THE SELECTION CRITERIA

The information about the investigation was to be given to victims who fulfilled the following conditions:

(1) had been exposed to rape or attempted rape;
(2) aged 16 year or over;
(3) resident in Oslo or immediate surroundings;
(4) had to be seen by the researcher within two weeks of the assault.

(For the definition of rape used in the present study see Chapter 2).

The age limit of 16 was chosen because in Norway this is the legal age of consent to participation in a sexual encounter with an adult. The geographical restriction was chosen so that the participant had a possibility for further contact with the researcher in an acute crisis, or to make sure that other help was provided, if necessary. The two-week time limit was chosen, both to provide time for those in a state of shock who did not seek help at once and to be flexible as regards arranging interviews with the participants when they felt up to it at a time that seemed chaotic for many of them, with lots of things to arrange.

Table 3.1 shows that 75 people (72 women and 3 men) fulfilled the criteria for participation: 72 of them received the invitation to participate (in 3 cases the staff forgot to hand out the information); 55 (76 percent) participated in the study. Of those, 48 (87 percent) had experienced complete rape (penetration) and 7 (13 percent) were recorded as attempted rape (no penetration); 32 (58 percent) had notified the police. Of the 17 others originally invited, only 5 refused to participate on the reply slip. Twelve accepted the invitation, but withdrew afterwards. Five of them informed about it, whereas seven did not turn up and could not be reached in spite of repeated attempts by post, telephone and/or informed network persons. In two of these cases the circumstances of the assault were unclear and the staff had some doubts about whether a rape had taken place. The researcher did not try to contact anyone at given addresses unannounced as this was considered unethical.

Table 3.1 *Uninvited, invited and participating victims who were registered as rape victims at the admission service of the Oslo Emergency Ward, 1 January–1 November 1990*

	No.
Registered victims	118
Did not meet the criteria for participation:	
due to geography 11	
due to time-limit 19	
due to age criteria 13	
	−43
Potential participants	75
Did not receive invitation/information	−3
Invited to participate	72
Refused or withdrew	−17
Participants: women 53, men 2	55

3.3.3. CHARACTERISTICS OF THE PARTICIPANTS

In the following presentation the two men (one completed homosexual rape and one attempted) are excluded although they were assessed and followed up in the same manner as the women. They were excluded from the presentation of the sample as well as from the results because they represented such a small group.

3.3.3.1. Sociodemographic Data

Age. The age range was 16–57 years, the mean age was 25.8, and the median age was 24. The age distribution is shown in Table 3.2.

Marital status and current living situation (Tables 3.3 and 3.4). Everyone who said they had a stable residence situation with a partner was recorded as cohabiting. The shortest cohabitant relationship had lasted 4 months, the longest 17 years. The shortest marriage had lasted one year, the longest 11 years.

Table 3.2 *Age distribution in the sample of rape victims presented in the study*

	Women	
Age	No.	%
16–19	11	21
20–29	28	53
30–39	11	21
≥40	3	5
Total	53	100

N = 53.

Table 3.3 *The distribution of marital status in the sample presented in the study*

Marital status	No.	%
Married	3	6
Cohabiting	8	15
Separated/divorced	13	25
Widowed	1	2
Single	28	53
Total	53	100

N = 53.

Table 3.4 *The distribution of current living situation in the sample presented in the study*

Current living situation	No.	%
With spouse/partner	11	21
With parents	7	13
Alone with children	7	13
With others	8	15
Alone	14	27
Other residence situation	6	11
Total	53	100

N = 53.

Current living situation focuses on a network factor, namely whom the participants live with. The reason for this choice was the assumption that network factors are important in relation to coping with traumatic experiences. "Living with others" were in all cases women who shared flats with peers. Three of the six women with "other residence situation" lived in institutions, one in a psychiatric after-care home, two in youth welfare homes. Three women had no permanent address and lived mainly in hostels.

Main employment. Higher education means at least three years' college or university education after completing secondary school (A level). The rest of the employed are put into one group. They were mostly employed in typical lower-income female jobs such as secretary, shop assistant, nurse or hospital assistant, waitress, etc. The group receiving benefits consisted of three disabled, two on rehabilitation benefits, one on mother's benefit and one on widow's pension. One of the unemployed defined herself as a temporary

Table 3.5 *The distribution of main employment situation in the sample presented in the study*

Main employment	No.	%
Student/pupil	12	23
Employment requiring higher education	8	15
Other employment	23	43
Receiving benefits	7	13
Unemployed	3	6
Total	53	100

N = 53.

housewife and was supported by her cohabitant; the other two received social welfare support.

3.3.3.2. Earlier health

Fourteen (26.5 percent) reported earlier psychiatric difficulties with functional impairment in the past. Half of them had received psychiatric treatment. Nine (17 percent) also had substance-abuse (two drug abuse, seven alcohol abuse) problems. Substance abuse was in all cases combined with earlier psychiatric difficulties with functional impairment, which means that 64 percent of the women with earlier psychiatric difficulties also had substance-abuse problems. Seven (50 percent) of these women had experienced sexual or physical abuse before the age of 12, and 11 (78 percent) before the age of 16.

Six (11 percent) had chronic somatic diseases and another two had had a serious somatic disease in the past.

3.3.4. THE REFUSAL GROUP

The information on this group is limited. The data registered with the Emergency Ward on current living situation were missing in three cases, and on work situation in two. They did not differ in a statistically significant way from the participant group on the sociodemographic data available at the ward. However, there were smaller differences. Slightly more of them were registered as married or cohabiting (29 percent) and unemployed (18 percent), and fewer were registered as living alone (18 percent). More of them were recorded as substance abusers (29 percent).

3.3.5. THE DROP-OUT GROUP

Six women dropped out of the study. Two of them had had psychiatric problems with functional impairment in the past and one suffered from alcohol dependency. Three of the six women were raped by an abusive partner.

3.4. Qualitative Method

For the analysis of the rape event narratives, a qualitative approach was chosen, namely a descriptive narrative approach (Polkinghorne, 1988; Mishler, 1986). Narrative is a widely used term.

The most inclusive meaning refers to any spoken or written presentation. A more specific meaning of the term is the kind of organizational scheme expressed in story form (Polkinghorne, 1988). The definition of narrative used in the present study is a more narrow definition used by Labov in relation to the analysis of narratives of personal experiences: "the recapitulation of experience that maintains the strict temporal ordering as it occurred in the real world" (Mishler, 1986). The object of the analysis is to abstract the theme or point of the story; the stories are inferred to be individual examples of more abstract and generalizable social interaction patterns (Polkinghorne, 1988). For further detilas about how the analysis was done in the present study, see Chapter 4.

3.5. Statistical Methods

In order to decide whether a mean change of differences of means in two groups were statistically significant, a two-sided Wilcoxon rank-sum test was used (Lehmann, 1975). This test was preferred to t-test because the variables did not show a "sufficient" normal distribution.

When comparing frequencies in two groups, a two-sided exact Fisher–Irwin test was applied (Kendall and Stuart, 1977). Factors predicting a long-term psychiatric outcome (predictors) were identified using a univariate statistical method (the exact Fisher–Irwin test). Logistic regression analysis was applied to construct the predictive indices based on several predictors (Kendall and Stuart, 1977). Each significant testing was carried out with a 5 percent significance level.

3.6. Summary

In order to answer the questions raised in the present study, a group of rape victims were assessed at three points in time. Efforts were made to gather information about the rape event as quickly and thoroughly as possible. The same was the case for the acute response, which could then form a basis for assessing changes in the reactions over time. Information about the person relevant to her physical and mental health as well as her social situation was collected as a basis for judging changes in health as well as relationships. Additionally the purpose of early information about the traumatic event, the acute response, the person and her network was to get data for the analysis of predictors at an early stage, comparable to the emergency situation, and before the course and the outcome related to health were known. The later assessments were done to measure and explore change and to evaluate outcome in terms of health indicators such as psychiatric symptoms, diagnosis and somatic symptoms. The information on coping collected at every assessment provided the possibility of looking at outcomes in relation to coping strategy.

Instruments that had demonstrated their usefulness, reliability and validity in traumatic stress studies were preferred. However, the interviews were designed to integrate new information and more exploratory methods were preferred when instruments did not seem to fit, or when the phenomena in questions had been only superficially described in earlier research.

The materials and methods will be discussed further in Chapter 11.

4

The Trauma of Rape – A Description of the Stressors

4.1. Introduction

In order to understand how rape can be a traumatic event – "an event outside the range of normal human experience that would be markedly distressing to almost anyone" – it is necessary to look more thoroughly into the victim's experience of the rape itself.

In the rape research literature, the impact of rape on the victim is most often explained by the fact that many rape victims experience a threat to their lives (Kilpatrick, Veronen and Best, 1985). The description of the trauma is usually limited to a recording of different components or variables present during the event. The emphasis on the overt violence as an important aspect of the rape experience as well as the clear categorization of rape as a violent crime represent a significant attempt to reduce the confusion surrounding the subject of rape. However, if threat to life is made the only explanation for the impact of rape, this oversimplification might represent a drawback in the treatment of victims by giving an inadequate basis for the understanding of what the victim has been through.

Clinical reports and treatment suggestions show a broad awareness of rape as more complex trauma (Rose, 1986). These aspects should also be explored in a research study. Researchers have been aware that there are different types of rape. Burgess and Holmstrom have categorized rapes into "blitz" rape and "confidence" rape (Burgess and Holmstrom, 1980). They emphasize the difference between a sudden attack with no interaction between victim and offender beforehand, and an attack where there has been a prior non-violent interaction between the involved parties. This typology is also used by Silverman and co-workers (Silvermann et al., 1988). Another categorization which has been used to look at rape differences is "stranger" rapes and "acquaintance" rapes, where stranger rapes are supposed to be more violent than acquaintance rapes, except for rapes by husbands and family members (Koss et al., 1988). These categorizations imply that one variable gives a different meaning to the rape event, although no evidence of this or descriptions of different patterns of the event as a whole have been displayed.

This chapter will therefore raise the following questions:

(1) Is rape an event outside the range of usual human experiences as described in criterion A of PTSD? How should the event be described and analysed when the aim is to understand its psychological impact?

(2) Which elements of the rape experience are identified and recognized as particularly stressful by the victims?

(3) Is it possible to categorize rape into different types based on different patterns in the victim's narrative of the rape event?

4.2. Method

4.2.1. THE RECAPITULATION OF THE EVENT

The traumatic event was recorded in a chronological model. In disaster psychiatry this has been named the time–spatial model, describing different stages of the disaster period (Weisæth, 1984). The stages have been given different names by different authors. In this study the information was recorded in the stages used by Weisæth: steady state, warning (a presentiment that something is wrong), threat (a definite cue of danger), impact (time of destruction), isolation (the time after the impact when the victim is alone) and rescue (Wallace, 1956; Weisæth, 1984).

The detailed interview about the rape event was conducted in the first assessment. The interviewer let the recapitulation follow the stages, and questions about the offender's behaviour and the emotions, thoughts and behaviour of the woman for every phase were secured. The components present during the different stages of the event were recorded, and will be presented as a component description. These categories were chosen beforehand, but could later be expanded or amended according to the new information the interview revealed. These categories were filled out either during the interview of afterwards from the tape.

4.2.2. DISTRESSING ELEMENTS

A question on what – in the the victim's own judgement – had been the worst part of the experience was also part of the first assessment. This question was repeated in the follow-up, along with questions about the content of flashbacks and other re-experiencing symptoms and questions about what in retrospect seems most unbearable to think about. The victims were also asked specifically whether they felt their life had been in danger, whether they were afraid of physical injuries, to what degree they felt violated, helpless or cheated. The final categorization of traumatic elements was established mainly from these data. However, the descriptions of thoughts and feelings during the different stages broadened the understanding of this information and supported the final categorization.

4.2.3. THE QUALITATIVE APPROACH

A rape event cannot be seen only as an impact agent, nor can its psychological impact on the victim be understood only through a presentation of variables present during the event. Rape represents an interaction between human beings. It can be described, in this context from the victim's perspective, by how the participants acted in order to influence each other's intentions and the accompanying thoughts or feelings of the victim. The event has a course, it changes over time, and the meaning of the components changes when the whole story is known. In the analysis of the rape event narrative, the researcher asked the same questions of every story. These questions stemmed from the awareness that what happened was an event between people, a social intercourse, related by one party. The following overall questions were asked of the narrative:

(1) What characterizes his behaviour towards her?
(2) What characterizes her response to his behaviour?
(3) In what position does that leave her?
   The detailed questions related to each stage in the narrative analysis will be presented with the results of the qualitative analysis.

Although the information about the rape event was collected in the first session (either taped and written down afterwards or written down during the interview), sometimes fragments and details turned up in later interviews. This information was included in the narrative analysis.

4.3. The Sequence of the Rape Trauma

Using the time–spatial model from disaster psychiatry, this model was adapted to the rape event. Change from one phase to another represents a major change in the offender's behaviour and/or a shift in the victim's perception of what was happening.

The first phase is **the situation before** and describes the situation the victim is in before the rape has started. The second phase, **the prelude**, includes both the warning and the threat phase of the time–spatial model. It is characterized by an introduction of something new which creates a feeling of uneasiness in the victim. There seemed no point in dividing the warning and the threat here, as the difference in the quality of the victim's experience was not distinct.

The impact period is divided into two phases, following a major qualitative shift in the experience when the victim either avoids the completion of the rape or surrenders. Thus a clear distinction between attempted and completed rape is possible. The third phase, **the attack**, describes the first part of the impact period. In this stage it becomes quite clear that the victim is assaulted. The fourth phase, **the carrying through**, describes the completion of the rape, the penetration.

The fifth phase, **the termination**, is the equivalent of the isolation and rescue phase and describes the end of the event.

4.4. A Component Description of the Rape Event

This description will present what happens during rape through a description of different components present in the different phases.

4.4.1. THE SITUATION OF THE VICTIM IMMEDIATELY BEFORE THE RAPE

Twenty-two victims (41 percent) were in a typical social situation with other people, e.g. in a restaurant or disco, attending a nachspiel, visiting somebody they knew or having visitors themselves. Fifteen (28 percent) were in an ordinary situation representing part of their daily routine, like being alone in their own home or on their way from one place to another. Six (11 percent) were asleep. Seven (13 percent) were abroad on holiday - two of them walking alone, the others in unfamiliar social situations. Three were in situations more difficult to classify.

4.4.1.1. Establishment of Contact Between Victim and Offender

Table 4.1 shows that in most cases contact was established through social contact. "Other" includes one who due to shock did not remember clearly how contact was established – she was found

Table 4.1 *Frequency of different modes of establishment of contact between victim and offender*

Mode of contact establishment	No.	%
Social contact	25	47
Long-lasting relationship	11	20
Blitz attack	14	27
Other	3	6
Total	53	100

N = 53.

Table 4.2 *Types of relational situation between victim and offender*

Relational situation	No.	%
Strangers	21	40
Superficial acquaintances	21	40
Friends or earlier partners	6	11
Existing partners or spouses	5	9
Total	53	100

N = 53.

naked in a ditch with clear evidence of sexual assault and remembered only fragments of the event. Another was assaulted by a cabdriver, thus the contact was established through a service relationship. The third found herself lost in a strange city and asked the offenders the way. In 28 (54 percent) cases the establishment of contact was marked by confidence-inducing strategies, e.g. the offender asked for help, advice, etc. or offered help.

4.4.1.2. Relationship Between Victim and Offender(s)

Table 4.2 demonstrates that strangers or superficial acquaintances represent the mode of relationship in the majority of the cases. Superficial acquaintances represent relationships where the people have met before, know each other by sight, or have been introduced by friends and/or have met and spent some time together socially before the prelude phase of the rape event.

4.4.1.3. Influence of Alcohol of Drugs on Offenders and Victims

Tables 4.3 and 4.4 demonstrate the frequency of influence of alcohol and/or drugs in offenders and victims before the rape event.

Table 4.3 *Frequency of recorded influence of alcohol and/or drugs on offender(s)*

Influence of alcohol/drugs	No.	%
Influenced	7	13
Not influenced	21	40
Uncertain	25	47
Total	53	100

N = 53.

Table 4.4. *Frequency of influence of alcohol and/or drugs on the victim before the rape event*

Influence of alcohol/drugs	No.	%
Slight influence (1 glass beer or wine)	11	21
Moderate influence (1–3 glasses beer or wine)	13	24
Considerable influence (>3 glasses beer/wine	—	—
Hard liquor or drugs	9	17
Not tasted any alcohol/drugs	20	38
Total	53	100

N = 53

The purpose of looking into this is to see whether use of alcohol plays an important role in the offender's behaviour, is a vulnerability factor for the victim and later is a risk factor in relation to outcome.

"Uncertain" means that the victims report that they did not see any intake of alcohol and/or drugs, are not certain that they smelt alcohol, or did not find the offender(s) very intoxicated, but think that the offender(s) might have been influenced or do not exclude the possibility.

4.4.1.4. Impression of the Offender(s)

The women's impression of the offenders before the rape varied. (Twelve (23 percent) women had no impression at all, which means that they did not see the offender(s) before the attack. Twenty-four (45 percent) had a neutral or a positive impression of the offender(s). Fifteen (28 percent) reported that they had a negative impression of the offender(s), regarding him (them) as unsympathetic, aggressive, dangerous or mad. One did not remember and one reported that she pitied the offender, who she felt was suffering

Table 4.5 *Characteristics and frequency of place of attack*

Place of attack	No.	%
Public place	19	36
Own home	11	21
Another home	17	32
Car	6	11
Total	53	100

N = 53

from mental anguish. Thus only a minority had a negative impression of the offender before the rape.

4.4.2. THE PRELUDE

Fourteen (26 percent) women could not afterwards recollect any identification of a warning. Three (6 percent) were not sure whether they had any presentiment that something was wrong. The rest had had some sensation of a warning. Six women could not identify what gave them this sensation, 27 attributed it to something the offender(s) said, did or their facial expression, four to other things, like the taste of a drink, behaviour of collaborators or appearance of a partner who from experience could be abusive.

The threat should be characterized by a clear sense of danger. Eighteen (34 percent) women reported that they did not experience any sense of danger before the attack; two did not remember. The threat was in all cases elicited by something the offender(s) said or did – for instance, refusing to stop the car, forcing entry to a room, verbal abuse, told he could be dangerous, refusing to leave when asked, etc.

4.4.3. THE ATTACK

The attack started with a clearly intentioned sexual advance in nine (17 percent) cases, e.g. kissing, stroking. In 38 (72 percent) the start had a more violent character, like seizing hard, pushing, slapping or kicking. Six (11 percent) were asleep and here the attack seemed to have started more gently.

The place where the attack occurred is indicated in Table 4.5. The table shows that in approximately half the cases the rape occurred in a private home.

Table 4.6 *Frequency and type of physical violence*

Violence	No.	%
No physical violence	3	6
Physical restraint, use of body weight or strength	15	28
Considerable physical violence (includes hitting, kicking, biting, blows, knifing, strangulation)	35	66
Total	53	100

N = 53

Table 4.6 indicates the use of physical violence. The three cases with no physical violence were all cases where the women were attacked in their sleep and the offenders let go immediately when the women woke up. Strangulation attempts were reported in 11 cases (20 percent) and were usually combined with other forms of violence. Verbal threats of physical harm or killing were reported in 16 cases (30 percent).

Weapons were used in 15 cases (29 percent), the most common being knives (11 cases).

4.4.4. THE CARRYING OUT OR PENETRATION PHASE

Forty-seven of the 53 women reported that they had been penetrated and were registered as exposed to completed rape. In the six cases of attempted rape, the women managed to avoid penetration or were helped by other people arriving on the scene. In five of the attempted rapes the woman reported one offender, in one case there were three. The number of offenders in the completed rapes were one in 36 cases (68 percent), two in seven cases (13 percent), three in two cases (4 percent), five in one case and seven in one case. The type and frequency of the sexual acts these offenders carried out are shown in Table 4.7.

Ejaculation did not always take place. Twenty-one (39 percent) reported that they felt sure the offender ejaculated during the penetration, 6 (11 percent) reported that the offender ejaculated after having interrupted the penetration, 13 (26 percent) reported that they were sure the offender had not ejaculated, and 12 (24 percent) reported they were not sure.

The women's impression of the offender(s) during the attack and carrying out phase is described in Table 4.8.

Table 4.7 *Type and frequency of reported sexual acts*

Sexual acts	No.	%
Touching, rubbing/no penetration	6	11
Penile vaginal penetration	37	70
Penile oral penetration	3	6
Both penile vaginal and oral penetration	3	6
Other combined sexual acts including penetration with objects	4	7
Total	53	100

N = 53

Table 4.8 *Victim's impression of offender(s) during attack and carrying out phase*

Impression of offender	No.	%
Don't know/cannot answer	9	17
Wanted to demonstrate power	8	15
Excited/enjoyed it	7	13
Two people (Dr Jeckyll/Mr Hyde)	2	4
Angry/mad/dangerous	27	51
Total	53	100

N = 53

4.4.5. THE TERMINATION

The event ended either through an initiative taken by the offender(s), through an initiative taken by the woman, by interference by others or a combination of several factors. In 20 (38 percent) cases the offender released the woman or fell asleep, so that it was possible for her to leave. In 11 (21 percent) cases the offender(s) made off. In 17 (32 percent) cases the woman managed to escape, in 4 (8 percent) cases others interfered and in the case where the woman was found in a ditch the termination is unclear.

This description of the components present during the event tells us what happens during a rape event through pieces of relevant information. For a more thorough understanding of the psychological meaning and impact of the rape it is necessary to present further material.

4.5. The Traumatic Elements

Several traumatic elements of the experience were mentioned by the women in the first interview.

4.5.1. THREAT OF PHYSICAL INJURY OR DEATH (VIOLATION OF PHYSICAL SAFETY)

Forty-two (79 percent) of the women reported that they had experienced a threat to their life during the rape; 20 (38 percent) felt that this was the worst part of the whole experience. The realization that another human being really was capable of injuring or killing them was a shocking, frightening experience and became the central stressful element of the rape event. This did not mean that they did not experience other elements as stressful too, but they did not give them the same significance. "The worst thing was that I felt they were capable of killing me – the feeling of terror connected to that. But it was also bad to be treated like that, as if I did not exist."

4.5.2. THREAT TO THEIR WORTHINESS AS HUMAN BEINGS (VIOLATION OF HUMAN WORTH)

Forty-eight (90.5 percent) reported that this was an important aspect of the experience. They reported that they felt dehumanized, treated like an object rather than a human being. Fourteen (26.4 percent) reported that this was the worst aspect of the experience and overshadowed everything else.

"The worst was to be treated like that, like something he could trample on."
"The worst was to be treated as if I was not a human being – I felt so worthless, they might just as well have killed me."
"It was more than a violation, he annihilated me as a person, a human being."

4.5.3. THREAT TO SEXUAL INTEGRITY (VIOLATION OF SEXUAL BOUNDARIES)

When penetration had taken place this was described as stressful in one way or another by nearly all the 47 women who had this experience. In five the issue was unclear; generally the distress was communicated more indirectly and was evidently more difficult to verbalize than, for example the fear of being killed.

"A terrible feeling, I cannot explain it."
"I felt nothing, no fear, nothing."
"It felt like I left my body and looked at the whole incident from above".

"I felt completely defeated, all my struggles had been in vain".
"I don't remember what I felt."
"I don't want to talk about it."

Although the penetration was reported to be difficult in one way or another by nearly all, only four (8 percent) women said initially that the penetration was the worst part of the experience.

4.5.4. THREAT TO CONTROL (VIOLATION OF PERSONAL CONTROL OVER OWN BODY AND LIFE)

The feelings connected with this were powerlessness and helplessness. Fifty (94 percent) women reported feeling some degree of helplessness connected with being powerless and robbed of control over what happened to them. Six (11 percent) said that this was the worst thing about the whole experience. They were in the younger age group of the sample. Examples of how this was expressed:

"He did not listen, whatever I said or did had no influence, I think that was the worst."
"The worst was that I could not control what happened, that a madman had me totally in his power."

4.5.5. THREAT TO CONFIDENCE AND TRUST (VIOLATION OF TRUST)

This included both trust in men and trust in oneself as a person able to evaluate other human beings.

"I cannot believe that he could fool me like that, that a person could change from being so nice to become an wild animal."
"How can a person change from being normal to become a monster; I will never be able to trust anybody again".
"And I thought they were my friends, if people are like that I don't see any point in being alive."

Twenty-seven (50 percent) felt they had been fooled or cheated by the offender(s). However, none of them said at the time of the first interview that this violation was the worst part of the experience.

4.5.6. ALTERNATIVE ANSWERS

Six women gave very personal answers as to what was the worst aspect of the experience; for example, "the fear", "the feeling of unreality when I woke up", "that he changed from a nice person to a monster", "not to understand what he wanted, the feeling of unpredictability", "the flashbacks of earlier experienced violence", "that he wanted me to suck him". Some of these answers can be interpreted as belonging to the above-mentioned stressors, but are not as clearly spelt out. For example, "that he changed from a nice person to a monster" is close to violation of trust.

Three women gave vague answers like "the whole experience", "I don't know, everything was awful", "I cannot explain, it was worse than everything I have ever experienced".

4.5.7. ADDITIONAL STRESS RELATED TO SEXUALITY

In the follow-up, one question in particular produced more information about the stressful elements of the event, namely: "When you think about the event, what is most unbearable or unpleasant to think about?"

Twenty-seven (57 percent) of the women answered with something related directly to the sexual content of the event, most often (15 women) related to the penetration itself ("when he entered me", "when he forced himself into my mouth"). However, other things related to sex were also mentioned – "the filthy words he used", "that he wanted me to suck him", "the way he touched me", "that he ejaculated on my stomach, his seed on my skin", "that I had sexual feelings in my dream, believing I made love to my lover and then woke up to find that awful stranger there", "the sight of his penis". Vaguer answers were: "I cannot bear to think about the sexual details"; "There are things I don't want to mention." Interviewer: "Sexual things?". "Yes, don't ask me – please."

For five women the answers on the unbearable corresponded with the worst aspect, or with the content of flashbacks. For example: worst – "that something was taken away from me, that intimate part I need to show love"; flashback – "I see myself from above, my behind sticking up in the air, being raped"; most unbearable to think about – "The moment he entered me." For the rest the answers did not correspond. For example: worst – "The worst was to be beaten and injured, that I felt he was capable of killing"; flashbacks – "I see his beating fist above my face, feel the blood running from my nose and the pain"; unbearable to think about – "The sexual part of it."

The women's accounts of what in their rape experience particularly caused distress have been presented here as the traumatic elements of the rape experience. However, in order to get a better picture of rape as a psychological stressor, a further description of the event as a comprehensive narrative is included.

4.6. A Narrative Analysis of the Rape Event: Patterns, Common Features and Variations

The recognition that the traumatic event represented an experience in relation to other human beings, an interactional event, led to questions concerning what characterized the offender's actions towards her, her responses to these actions and in what position this put her. Thus the following analysing questions were asked of each narrative:

1. *The situation before*:
   In what kind of situation is the victim just before the rape happens?
   (a) The relationship. Who is (are) he (they) to her?
   (b) What does he take advantage of? What right of hers does he thereby disregard?
   (c) What does that make of her?
2. *The prelude*:
   (a) Does he do anything that makes her think/sense that something is wrong?
   (b) How does she react to this (actions, thoughts, feelings)?
   (c) Who is she then, or what does that make of her?
3. *The attack*:
   (a) How does he attack?
   (b) What is her reaction to this (thoughts, feelings, actions)?
   (c) Who is she then, or what does that make of her?
4. *The carrying out*:
   (a) What does he do?
   (b) What is her reaction to this (thoughts, feelings, actions)?
   (c) Who is she then, or what does that make of her?
5. *The termination*:
   (a) What action indicates the ending?
   (b) What is her reaction to this (thoughts, feelings, actions)?
   (c) Who is she then, or what does that make of her?

The following example of an analysis of a rape-event narrative is presented in order to give the reader an opportunity to see how the narrative analysis was conducted.

Example: Ann is a 25-year-old biology student, single and lives alone in her own flat. She contacts the Emergency Ward on the evening of her return from Stockholm, where she was raped the night before. She had notified the police directly after the assault and had at the request of the police been examined by a gynaecologist. She now contacts the ward because she feels highly distressed and disturbed by continuous flashbacks of the assault. She asks for help to cope with her psychological reaction, which overwhelms and frightens her. The story was not told as fluently as it is presented here.

I was on this tour with the university handball team, participating in the inter-Nordic cup. The last evening we went out to celebrate. I drank more wine than I usually do. Suddenly I felt very tired and wanted to go back to the hotel, but nobody else wanted to leave yet, so I went out alone. When I came out on the pavement, I could not remember the way back to the hotel. Two young men stood there next to a van. They looked alright, ordinary. I asked them about the way. They explained. Then one of them said: "We are going in the same direction, we can give you a lift, it is not safe to walk alone in this area so late at night." I felt grateful and accepted the lift. All three of us sat in the front; I sat next to the door. Suddenly I recognized a house quite close to the hotel. At the same time they pointed in the direction of the hotel and laughed between them. I suddenly felt very scared and sober, thought I had been stupid to accept the lift. I tried to keep my voice calm when I told them to stop, I could find my way now. They did not answer, did not look at me, just increased the speed of the van. I repeated my request several times, they ignored me, their faces were immobile, like masks. I thought of jumping out of the van, but the speed was high, I would certainly be injured, probably killed. There was hardly any traffic, we were already on a highway. I thought about what they wanted, whether they would kill me, felt so scared, so helpless; totally in their power. I asked them several times to stop and let me go and got no response, it was as if I did not exist. They talked between themselves now; about where to go. After about ten minutes they left the main road and turned off onto a smaller road heading towards some woodland. After what seemed an endless drive, we came up an alley, to a parking lot. When the van stopped, I immediately jumped out and started to run. It was an impulse, I really did not believe I could make it. They came after me, both of them, One grasped me, the other pulled a knife. They told me to do what they said, or else . . . and flashed the knife in front of my face. I thought then that they probably wanted to rape me, but what were they going to do to me afterwards? Would they kill me? I thought they must be mad. I thought I had to be careful, not provoke their anger, remain passive, subordinate. I felt paralysed by fear. For my own sake though, I protested meekly. They pushed me back to the van and into the back. They pulled off my tights and pants. I had my period. When they saw the sanitary pad, they swore and said bah, as if disgusted. I felt so humiliated. I closed my eyes and kicked carefully, to show my resistance without provoking too much. Suddenly one of them seized my jaws and forced his penis in my mouth. He held my head and jaws and pushed and pushed. I had no thoughts, was not scared anymore, it was just terrible, disgusting. I think I fainted for a few seconds. Then I felt the salty taste in my mouth and he pulled back. He turned to the other one: "your turn." I thought it was over, tried to tell myself that it could not get worse. He was not very excited, tried, but said he felt repulsed by me. I thought: I am shit to them, I felt so humiliated. They both seemed to lose interest then. I thought of getting away, no time for emotions. I quietly got up, out of the van, they did not seem to notice. I started to run, barefoot in the cold, on the gravel, feeling no pain, I remember noticing that. Tears started to stream, I felt I was running for my life, towards some lights. When I reached a house, I rang the bell and sat down on the step and cried and cried. A man came with a dog. I cried and asked for help. He took me into the house, his wife came and wrapped a rug around me. Then – I knew I was safe.

Analysis:

1. *The situation before*:
   She is alone in the street of an unfamiliar town and cannot find her way.
   (a) Who are they to her? They are two young men she did not know existed before they happen to be there when she needs assistance.
   (b) They take advantage of her being alone in an unfamiliar place, in a vulnerable position. They thereby disregard her right to move freely and ask for information when it is needed.
   (c) It put her into the position of a prey.

2. *The prelude*:
   (a) They are not acting according to their promises. From then on they ignore her as a person in her own right.
   (b) She blames herself, feels frightened and helpless. Thinks of escape and evaluates it as too dangerous. Thinks of control and acts with verbal intervention. When the opportunity occurs she tries flight, triggered by fear.
   (c) It put her into the position of an object deprived of human rights. When she flees her role is the role of a hunted prey.
3. *The attack*:
   (a) They grab her and threaten her verbally and with a weapon.
   (b) She thinks of what they might be capable of doing, appraises them to be capable of killing. She feels fear and helplessness. Thinks of subordination as a solution. Makes weak protest to retain her own self-respect.
   (c) This makes her a victim, an object of their aggression. At the same time, appraising the situation, she becomes her own protector.
4. *The carrying out*:
   (a) They reject the vaginal entrance to her body because of her menstrual blood. They choose to invade her body forcibly through her mouth.
   (b) She has no conscious thoughts. Feelings of fear disappear and are replaced by feelings of disgust and shame.
   (c) Her position is the role of a dehumanized object.
5. *The termination*:
   (a) They forget her, lose interest after the use of her.
   (b) Her thoughts and feelings are focused on escape.
       She makes an active escape in search of help and safety. In doing this she feels fear, despair and in the end release.
   (c) They put her in the position of a used object deprived of human dignity. Her own action makes her her own rescuer and she ends up as a survivour.

Based on the qualitative analysis of every rape-event story two main patterns of rape narrative emerge: the violent rape and the sexual rape. Those who described the *death threat* as the worst experience had rape-event stories that coincided most with pattern 1. Those who described *violation of worth* as the worst aspect, had stories that coincided mostly with pattern 2. For the remainder there was no link between what was experienced as worst and the pattern they belonged to.

4.6.1. PATTERN 1: THE VIOLENT RAPE

The main characteristic of the violent rape is the sudden violent attack in the attack phase. The subgroups A, B and C represent different variants of the violent rape.

4.6.1.1. Variant A: the Violent Rape with a Stranger (16 women – 12 rapes, 4 attempted rapes)

The situation of the victim before the rape is that the woman is vulnerable, being either alone or in company with one or two strange men. The offender is a stranger. In five cases there is more than one offender. The stranger(s) takes advantages of the fact that the woman is unprotected, she is an easy prey, and her role is just that – a prey.

Often the prelude phase is missing; there is no contact between offender and victim before the attack. The woman may afterwards say that she felt a vague sense of uneasiness before the attack, for example a feeling of being followed or watched.

The prelude may also start through a more normal interaction between victim and offender with a question or an offer of assistance. When this produced uneasiness in the victim, she would typically disregard it, thinking that she was irrational, and continue to behave as if nothing was wrong. When thus her common sense fails to evaluate the danger of the situation, she takes on the role of a naive person, one who cannot appraise what is dangerous.

The attack is the most specific in this pattern of rapes. It starts suddenly and brutally, either by threat with a weapon or by violent physical attack. The violence seems absurd to the woman and most often not connected to what had happened prior to the attack. Her response is marked by surprise and shock; what is happening is unreal, incomprehensible. The offender's intention of rape is not communicated clearly during the attack. Resistance through fight or flight reactions is met by increased violence. What stops the violence is subordination. Most women choose subordination sooner or later in the process in order to stop the violence. The feelings of helplessness and powerlessness aroused in this phase become even more intense in the next phase. Many women try to communicate with the offender, try to "reach him", to negotiate, to beg, to play for time, to calm him down. They feel that he cannot be reached, that he rejects human contact. This not only makes her feel powerless, but often the feeling of being regarded as a non-person, an object, starts here.

Four women belonging to this group succeeded in their efforts to avoid the next phase. All of them had previous experience of violence, two of them having been raped before. They all took considerable risks in order to escape from the situation. Somewhere between the attack and the carrying through phase the intention to rape has been clearly communicated and understood by the victim. The offender threatens, forces the woman to obey by continuing the threat to injure and kill, either verbally or behaviourally or both, until she gives in. A weapon can be held against her body, or hands around her throat to keep her quiet.

Most often the offender forces the woman to vaginal intercourse, but he can also demand other services like other positions, oral stimulation, oral intercourse or anal intercourse. Penetration can also be done with objects in addition to penile penetration. Ejaculation does not always take place. Some offenders will shower verbal and non-verbal expressions of despise upon the woman during the penetration. Others can suddenly express tender words contrasting completely with the brutal behaviour of the preceding moment. If not before, in the course of this phase the woman understands that her choice is subordination or risking her life. Her impression of the offender is that he is mad, split into two people, or just very hostile and angry. In some cases she manages to refuse or avoid certain acts that are demanded of her, but not the penetration itself. The feeling of powerlessness and helplessness is mostly overwhelming, but to have decided something or disobeyed something actively demanded of her can give a limited sense of control. The treatment she is subjected to is mostly experienced as humiliating and shameful, but the feeling of being in danger is more prominent. During penetration, however, there is a marked change in feelings: the fear and anxiety are replaced by intense feelings of helplessness, defeat, emptiness or dissociation. The woman's role in this phase is the role of a non-human object, or a despised being.

The rape ends with the offender either leaving the scene, losing interest or not letting her go. In the last case the termination phase can go on for hours before it ends with a successful escape by the woman when the offender is less on guard. Some offenders threaten reprisals when they leave: "If you leave this place before . . . ," or, "If you tell the police, I will come back and kill you!" Some might deliver a message that is confusing for the woman, e.g. demanding money, taking clothes or jewellery, thanking her, giving a compliment, asking for punishment.

An active escape makes the woman her own rescuer; left by the offender she becomes the used object. In either case she is not safe until a secure shelter has been found. That is what directs her behaviour at the end of this phase and her final role becomes that of the survivor.

4.6.1.2. Variant B: the Violent Rape with a Social Beginning (12 women – 11 rapes, 1 attempted rape)

This variant of the violent rape differs only in the prior situation, which is characterized by a social encounter, for example out with friends at a disco or a restaurant or invited somewhere with people she knows.

The offender is someone she has not met before, but becomes acquainted with the same evening, a superficial acquaintance as in pattern 2. In a few cases there is more than one offender. He can be a dancing partner or just someone who starts to chat. He is often experienced as nice; in a few cases he is looked upon as a potential sweetheart. He takes advantage of the normality of the situation, the normal interaction between men and women. He thereby disregards her right to function as an independent, equal human being.

She might feel a slight uneasiness because of something the offender says or does, e.g. when he displays domineering behaviour, but she has no sense of danger. Again this puts her in the position of a naive person, not able to judge other people.

The attack phase starts as in variant A, suddenly and violently, out of context, impossible to comprehend. The sexual intent is not immediately communicated, the incomprehensible violence dominates the scene. Only in one case does the woman understand the violence as a reaction to her communication of not wanting sex with the offender. The woman's response is again dominated by surprise and shock. From here on the pattern is the same as described in variant A.

4.6.1.3. Variant C: the Violent Partner Rape (5 Women, 5 Rapes)

A small subgroup of five women are alone in their home with their spouse/partner in the situation before the rape. The relationship to the offender is that of spouse or partner. The partner takes advantage of being alone with her in a private situation, where nobody will interfere. Her role is that of a scapegoat, one who will be punished.

The prelude phase is long in this type of rape, the atmosphere tense, the offender communicates disapproval of something she has said or done and she knows from experience that sooner or later the abuse will start, but not how and when. She expects abuse, but not rape. What she tries to do is aimed at avoiding the abuse. This puts her in the position of an oppressed person.

The attack phase starts as in the other types of violent rape, suddenly and violently. The physical violence is severe, including a combination of several violent acts, such as kicking, hitting, punching, throwing, stranglehold and in one case attempted strangulation with a scarf. The youngest of these women, where the abuse has not lasted more than a few months, fights back. Two beg for mercy. The others remain passive, subordinate, knowing from experience that resistance increases violence. Two of the women hope they will be killed, as they cannot see any other way out of the abuse. The emotional response of the women at the end of this phase is dominated by feelings of helplessness and hatred. The role of these women is to be a punch ball, a target for the outlet of frustration, aggression and hate, confirming both the offender's ability to dominate and his defeat.

The penetration takes place when the woman has been beaten thoroughly and expects that the abuse has stopped. Her verbal objection is not taken seriously. She does not try to resist physically, knowing that this will start the violence again. Her emotional response is a feeling of emptiness, shame or dissociation. The act is also experienced as a final deceit, destroying both what is left of their mutual love and her sense of herself as a human being.

The offender typically does not let the woman leave after the rape. The women either wait until the offender has fallen asleep and then escape, or they manage to contact someone. In all these cases the rape represents a final act of deceit and violation and results in help-seeking behaviour. The woman ends up as an active participant in her own rescue operation.

4.6.2. PATTERN 2: THE SEXUAL RAPE (20 WOMEN — 19 RAPES, 1 ATTEMPTED RAPE)

The phases are the same as above and many features are similar. The differences can be described as follows.

The situation before is characterized by social interaction or a familiar situation where the woman thinks she is safe. She is together with people she has some knowledge of in a restaurant, in another home, or she is close to or in her own home, or she is fast asleep. The offender(s) is in the majority of cases a superficial acquaintance, but can also be somebody she knows better, or a former partner. In two cases he is a stranger: one case is an attempted rape and in the other a stranger gets into the woman's room when she is asleep. There may be more than one offender in these types of rape (four cases with two offenders). The offender takes advantage of her confidence in the situation. The woman's role is that of a naive part in a play she is not aware of.

The prelude phase is dominated by confidence-inducing strategies: the offender offers help, comfort or support in an unpleasant situation, or makes an appeal for help or support – for example, he has to talk to her, is unhappy, needs someone to talk to. When this phase is missing, it is because the woman is asleep. The woman chooses to trust the offender and if she feels suspicion she attributes this to a negative side of herself. Only in one case with the stranger does the woman refuse the help he asks for and recommend another solution.

The attack phase can start with a sexual approach or a sexualized violent approach where the sexual intent is clearly communicated. The use of force is not unnecessarily brutal; mostly it concerns holding, use of physical restraint or body weight. Verbal threats can, for example, be about showing who has the power, or vague "if you don't do as I say you will regret it". Direct threats about killing or threats with weapons do not occur. Characteristically no more power than is necessary to achieve the aim of subordination is used. However, physical resistance is met with increased violence, such as stranglehold or demonstration of more strength. The woman's emotional responses usually start with uneasiness, slight fear and often surprise. However, she can also be irritated and angry and is less likely to feel paralyzed. Her behavioural response is typically verbal or physical resistance, often confident that, when the offender understands that she does not want what he asks for, he will stop. The feeling of being in danger, and the intense fear connected with that, come more slowly as her resistance is met by increased violence. When the woman is asleep, the attack starts cautiously; she usually wakes up as a result of the feeling of bodyweight or because she is penetrated. Two of the women who were attacked in their sleep first had sexual dreams about making love to their partners, then felt in the dream that something was wrong and woke up. All the offenders disregard the woman's right to decide over her own body.

The penetration phase is not qualitatively different from that described for pattern 1. The conclusion that subordination is the only way out of it and the emotions connected with the penetration are the same. The typical shift in emotions from fear to resignation, emptiness, numbness or dissociation is described in these rapes in much the same way as in pattern 1. The sexual acts are more likely to be restricted to vaginal intercourse. With more offenders this might be extended. However, the similarity to normal sexual intercourse is closer, although the woman's emotions connected to it are very different. The woman's experience of the offender during the rape is never that of a dangerous madman. The impression rather is that the offender was angry, or that he wanted to demonstrate power or that he enjoyed himself. Her role becomes that of a used object in the hands of a domineering, unpleasant variant of a normal man who deprives her of her human rights and worth and transforms her into a non-person. Typically for this pattern, the rape does not last very long and the offender dismisses the woman as soon as it is over. The impression that she is a used object without further value is reinforced.

Two main patterns of rape events have been described. One is characterized by a violent attack with three variants regarding the pre-rape situation and victim/offender relationship. The other is characterized by a sexualized attack approach.

4.7. Discussion

The methods and results in the present chapter will also be discussed later (see Chapter 11). The present discussion will mainly concern the three modes of description of rape as a psychological stressor.

In order to understand how a rape event can have a psychological impact on the victim, a component description of different variables or components present during the different stages of the event was performed. The component description gives a quantitative recording of variables and is enough to give a clear impression of the main features of the event as an experience of force and violence – a serious threat to one's life or physical integrity. The A criterion as defined in the DSM-III-R description of PTSD is thus most often present.

A description of the rape through a description of variables is the traditional form of presentation in research literature. It has the advantage of providing a basis for statistical analysis, for example of predictive factors in relation to indicators of health. Its disadvantage is that it decontextualizes the traumatic event into bits and pieces. Thus it reveals little of the meaning of the traumatic event as a psychological experience, and forms too weak a basis for knowledge of specific traumatic elements and for understanding the event as an experience in relation to another/other human being(s).

The second mode of description of the traumatic elements comes closer to a psychological understanding of the trauma of rape. It is based on information from both open-ended questions as well as more specific question and answer categories. Whereas violation of physical safety, violation of control, violation of trust and violation of worth are features that are more or less part of any violent trauma, the violation of the person as a sexual being is specific. This violation can not only be one of the factors in the traumatic experience, but probably gives a different meaning to the whole event. This again demonstrates the difficulty arising when one tries to categorize elements of a traumatic experience.

The third mode of description, based on analysis of narratives, has the ambition of describing the event as a unity – a human experience with other human beings. Through a comprehensive focus on the victim's response to the offender's actions, a better understanding of her experience can be achieved and enhances the understanding of the traumatic elements.

In the narrative description of the rape, however, the stressor becomes more than the traumatic elements; it can be seen as a violent, forced, degrading, confusing and ambiguous piece of human sexual interaction. The most common feature in the emotional experience, regardless of pattern, is the description of emotions connected to the forced penetration; the shift from fear to emptiness, numbing or dissociation reveals fragments of an emotional experience not fully understood in this study. Forced penetration can be seen as a simultaneous threat to physical, psychological and sexual integrity. The invasion of her body can be interpreted not only as depriving her of her human dignity, but as removing her right to own her body and to possess an independent sexuality. The confusion surrounding the issue of rape might more than anything be linked to this theme: who are to be defined as the owners of women's bodies and their sexuality? The present study indicates that, to women, the emotional experience of being forcibly penetrated has a distinct psychological impact. This also emphasizes that the distinction between attempted and completed rape is of relevance.

The classification of different types of rape through the narrative analysis makes them contextual and relative to each other. Polkinghorne rightly points out that the identification of a narrative as a member of a category cannot be the same in the human realm of meaning as in natural and biological sciences. The typologies should simply be considered as statements of similar events that are shared by various stories (Polkinghorne, 1988).

Compared with earlier categorizations, the present study indicates that an acquaintance rape or confidence rape may have a sudden and violent attack phase (a blitz attack) and that a blitz rape can be non-violent (attack in sleep). Thus thorough exploration of the events reveals that the social intercourse of a rape event is less obvious or straightforward than earlier presentations have assumed.

Whereas the narrative description produces better information and understanding concerning the psychological impact and meaning of rape and consequently will be useful for the clinician treating rape victims, it also has disadvantages. In a study like the present one, which looks for changes in health, the direct connection between this understanding and changes in health is more difficult to analyse.

The follow-up part of the present study will investigate whether factors in the rape situation will have a predictive value for different outcomes regarding mental health; for this purpose the component description will be valuable. However, the aim of describing the pattern of a rape event is, as mentioned before, to give a better understanding of rape as a stressor, regardless of the relation to outcome.

4.8. Conclusion

In order to understand the psychological impact of rape, three modes of analysing and describing the traumatic event were applied: a component description, a description of the traumatic elements and a descriptive narrative analysis. Each mode of description contributes to the understanding of rape as a stressor and completes the picture of "an event outside the range of normal human experience, an event that would be distressing to almost anyone". The traumatic elements such as violation of physical safety, of human worth, of personal control and of trust are elements inherent in any violent trauma. The sexual content and the violation of sexual boundaries attach another meaning to the whole event and differentiate it from other violent traumas.

Another specific feature which becomes clear in the descriptions of the patterns of the rape events is how they represent a distortion of human sexual interaction. Being at the same time similar to and different from normal sexual intercourse, the rape will be experienced as exceedingly confusing and difficult to assess.

5

The Acute Response to Rape

5.1. Introduction

All studies of immediate psychological reactions to rape seem to agree on the finding that fear and anxiety are the most prominent responses (Katz and Mazur, 1979). The reaction has been described either as a crisis reaction (Burgess and Holmstrom, 1974) or as a classical conditioned response to a life-threatening situation (Kilpatrick et al., 1979). Some studies have emphasized the depressive reaction (Atkeson et al., 1982). Although some authors have suggested it retrospectively, what has not been documented in relation to these studies is whether the immediate response to rape could be a post-traumatic stress reaction with the specific features described in Post-Traumatic Stress Disorder (PTSD) (DSM-III-R, 1987).

The main characteristic of *an acute crisis reaction* is a mental state of disequilibrium usually dominated by feelings of distress and helplessness, leading to a breakdown in adaptation (Caplan, 1961). The main characteristics of *an acute post-traumatic stress reaction* are more specific, with intrusive re-experience of the trauma, persistent avoidance of stimuli associated with the trauma or numbing responses, as well as symptoms of increased arousal (DSM-III-R, 1987). A crisis reaction is not a post-traumatic stress reaction; it may be elicited by a number of distressing life-events. An acute post-traumatic stress reaction is elicited by a traumatic experience "that would be markedly distressing to almost anyone". The consequence may well be a state of crisis, but the features of the reaction will include more specific characteristics.

The discussion in relation to treatment has focused on crisis intervention or a cognitive behavioural approach (Kilpatrick et al., 1982). If, however, the reaction is to be understood as a post-traumatic stress reaction, the recollection and effort of coping with the memory of the event will have to be emphasized much more in the treatment. The victim's immediate reaction to the trauma of rape therefore needs to be looked into once more.

This chapter will therefore address the following questions:

(1) Does the acute response to rape or attempted rape follow the pattern of a general post-traumatic stress reaction to severe trauma?

(2) Does the response have specific features of importance for clinical practice?

5.2. Method

The results presented in this chapter stem from the first assessment conducted within two weeks of the assault. A description of this assessment is presented in Chapter 3. Here particular emphasis will be laid on the ratings of post-traumatic stress symptoms on CPRS–PTSD and the ratings on the three self-assessment instruments, IES (Impact of Event Scale), STAI x-1 (State Anxiety, 12 items) and SSL (stress-symptom list, Leymann).

All victims were interviewed in the first two weeks after the assault had taken place. The median day for the interview was the fifth day after the assault.

5.3. Results

According to the CPRS–PTSD scores, the majority of the patients suffered from intrusive re-experiencing of the traumatic event. About half of them also reported bad dreams and nightmares. Some efforts to avoid thoughts, feelings or activities which reminded them of the rape were seen in all subjects. The majority also suffered from increased arousal; in particular, difficulty falling or staying asleep, concentration problems, hypervigilance and exaggerated startle response were frequent (Table 5.1).

Accordingly 77 percent of the patients reported intrusion at a high level of distress on the intrusion subscale of IES (Table 5.2). Avoidance was more evenly distributed between moderate and high levels of distress, no subject having a low level of avoidance (Table 5.2).

Signs of anxiety were, in addition to the increased arousal symptoms, also scored on the CPRS item "inner tension", where 68 percent scored at the highest intensity level. The mean value on STAI x-1 (state anxiety) was 36.4 (SD:6.85), range 20–48. There was a significant correlation between state anxiety and intrusion, $p < .001$. Fear of actual repetition or a new assault was expressed by 71 percent of the subjects. Fear of being alone was expressed by

Table 5.1 *Distribution of CPRS scores (indicating intensity of symptoms) on nine post-traumatic stress symptoms in victims of rape in the acute phase*

CPRS item	Zero/min. No.	%	CPRS score Moderate No.	%	High No.	%
Intrusive re-experiencing	2	4	13	25	38	71
Bad dreams/nightmares	25	47	2	4	26	49
Trauma-avoidance	0	0	24	45	29	55
Loss of interest	9	17	24	45	20	38
Difficulties falling or staying asleep	11	21	11	21	34	64
Irritability/aggression	23	43	22	42	8	15
Difficulty concentrating	9	17	16	30	28	53
Hypervigilance	4	8	7	13	42	79
Exaggerated startle response	6	11	10	19	37	70

N = 53

Table 5.2 *Distribution of Impact of Event Subscale scores at different levels of distress in victims of rape in the acute phase*

Impact of Event Subscale	Low No.	%	Level of distress Medium No.	%	High No.	%
Intrusion (N = 50)	2	4	10	20	38	76
Avoidance (N = 47)	0	0	21	45	26	55

58 percent. Aggression was not a prominent emotion in the majority of cases, 46 percent having low levels of aggression (6–12), 36 percent medium levels (13–18) and 18 percent high levels (19–24) on the aggression scale (STAGI), mean 13 (SD: 5), range 6–24. On the CPRS irritability/aggressive feelings the scores were similar (see Table 5.1).

Dissociative symptoms, especially depersonalization, were also experienced by many victims, not only during the event, but also in the acute phase: 45 percent experienced moderate depersonalization and 36 percent were found to have extremely high levels of depersonalization on CPRS.

Psychophysiological stress symptoms, both autonomic and muscular responses, were frequent and recorded at moderate or high intensity levels in 89 percent (autonomic responses) and 95 percent (muscular reactions) on CPRS. The self-reported data obtained by SSL revealed the same response. The most frequent bodily symptoms in the first few days after the assault were tremor, nausea, headache, sweating, dizziness and palpitations (Table 5.3).

Table 5.3 *Self-reported frequency of bodily reactions in the first few days after the assault*

Bodily reaction	No.	%
Headache	32	60
Dizziness	30	57
Tremor	39	74
Muscle-ache	24	45
Nausea	40	75
Vomiting	20	38
Stomach-ache	24	45
Diarrhoea	12	23
Sweating	31	58
Palpitations	28	53
Breathing difficulties	17	32

N = 53

The majority of the patients also reported depressive symptoms. On the 10-item Montgomery–Åsberg Depression Rating Scale (MADRS; see Chapter 3), 22 percent showed mild depressive scores (10–19), 54.5 percent signs of moderate depression (20–34) and 23.5 percent signs of severe depression (35–60). The most frequent symptoms were reduced sleep, reported sadness, difficulties concentrating and loss of interest, but suicidal thoughts were also frequent, 34 percent having suicidal thoughts within a moderate intensity range, 29 percent at a high intensity range. Few confided these thoughts spontaneously, and they were not picked up by the emergency staff. The content of the suicidal thoughts was unusually violent for female patients, e.g. cutting their veins, shooting, hanging or throwing themselves in front of cars or trains.

Guilt about behaviour needed to survive the rape and self-blame for the circumstances prior to the event were felt at a moderately severe level in 25 percent, and a high level of severity in 60 percent. Shame was present at a moderately severe level in 33 percent, and at a high severity level in 58 percent. Whereas feelings of guilt and self-blame in the majority of cases were uttered spontaneously, feelings of shame were uttered with reluctance. Compulsive acts related to the event all involved compulsive washing and cleaning of the body, reported by 40 percent.

5.4. Discussion

The present study confirms that the acute psychological reaction to rape shows the typical symptom pattern of a post-traumatic stress reaction in the acute phase. The symptoms are the same as those described in DSM-III-R for Post-Traumatic Stress Disorder (DSM-III-R, 1987). The last PTSD criterion, namely duration, is not fulfilled. However, early detection of a severe post-traumatic stress reaction and consequently choice of treatment strategy could be of importance for the prognosis.

The distinction between numbing responses and depression is difficult, especially in the acute phase. A depressive symptom like loss of interest is also a numbing response. Sleep disturbances and difficulties in concentrating can be a post-traumatic stress symptom indicating increased arousal, but may also be symptoms of depression. However, depressive symptoms in general and especially suicidal ideation, shame and guilt reactions are less frequently reported among victims who have experienced accidents and disaster (Malt and Olafsen, 1992; Weisæth, 1984; Holen et al., 1983). Such reactions have been reported in victims who have been exposed to violence, including humiliating and degrading treatment by other human beings (Krupnick and Horowitz, 1980). This supports the assumption that a depressive reaction is an independent feature in the acute response to rape. Whether this reflects specific characteristics of the psychological trauma or is induced by cultural attitudes towards victims of violence, especially sexual violence, or both, remains to be clarified.

Psychophysiological reactions are usual in the acute post-traumatic phase and the reactions recorded in this material do not differ essentially from other Norwegian studies of acutely traumatized persons, except that nausea seems to be a more prominent symptom (Weisæth, 1984).

The violent content of the suicidal ideation could suggest that clinicians receiving female patients with a background of violent suicidal attempts should ask specifically about rape or violent traumas in their history.

The level of distress in the subjects of this study is high compared with other populations that have been in dangerous and life-threatening situations. In Malt's study of people injured in accidents, only 1.9 percent had scores above 36 on STAI x-1 in the acute phase, the mean score in the present sample. Only 4.9 percent in Malt's study had intrusion subscale scores above 19 (the highest level of distress), whereas 76 percent in the present sample had scores above 19 (Malt and Olafsen, 1992). The results are more comparable with Weisæth's study of tortured sailors, where 54 percent had intrusive symptoms in the first four weeks after their release and intrusion subscale scores above 19 on IES six months afterwards (Weisæth, 1989). This indicates that the impact of rape as a trauma is severe.

In the present study, the time between trauma and interview varied from 2 to 14 days, so that the interview could well have caught subjects at slightly different stages in their reaction. However, it is doubtful whether it is possible to do this kind of study within a closer time range without losing the victims who, owing to shock and shame reactions, do not contact anybody for the first few days. In addition research regulations requiring written consent from participants before they are allowed to be contacted rule out the possibility of a researcher participating in, for example, an emergency admission. Where no service for victims exists, direct referrals from the police could be a quicker route. The sample would then be more selective. Compared with other studies, only one study is more accurate in this respect (6–10 days), and here the participation rate is lower (45 percent) (Kilpatrick et al., 1979). The experience from the present study was that the researcher had to be flexible in order to get participation, being prepared both to see people quickly as well as to wait, according to the needs of the victims.

In earlier studies the trauma of rape has mainly been understood as a reaction to a life-threatening experience (Kilpatrick et al., 1979; Burgess and Holmstrom, 1974). The present study of immediate reactions as a post-traumatic stress response, with special depressive features such as frequent suicidal ideation, shame and guilt reactions, supports the results presented in the previous chapter that the psychological content of the trauma is more complicated, a suggestion also made by psychotherapists (Rose, 1986). There is also a need for more research to identify risk factors for developing long-lasting PTSD and other psychosocial problems, which can be picked up in the emergency situation. This can only be clarified through the follow-up study. Identifying subjects at risk in the acute phase will enable clinicians to focus therapeutic efforts especially towards this group.

Whereas mental health services for rape victims are established and accepted in the United States this is not so in Europe. The present study confirms that victims of rape in the acute phase are highly distressed and that, according to their CPRS–PTSD scores, at least 71 percent are in need of a mental health service in the acute phase and the others have to be further evaluated. No one is unaffected. The results also indicate that the treatment approach should take into consideration the specific post-traumatic stress nature of the response, which means that crisis intervention alone is not sufficient. The attitude and behaviour of the therapist will probably be of great importance when feelings like shame and guilt are so prominent. In clinical practice, emphasis should therefore be focused on how the victim should be approached in the acute stage so that acceptance can be communicated and the right to services confirmed.

5.5. Conclusion

The findings in the present study suggest that the acute response to rape, in the majority of the victims, follows the pattern of a post-traumatic stress reaction with the specific symptoms described in DSM-III-R as Post-Traumatic Stress Disorder. Features that seem more prominent in victims of rape than in victims of accidents or disaster are shame, guilt and suicidal ideation. The severity of symptoms indicates that the impact of rape as a trauma is considerable, at least among patients seeking assistance in an emergency ward. The present findings also indicate a need for a mental health service for victims of rape as well as specific treatment procedures that take into consideration the post-traumatic stress nature of the response.

6

The Course of the Long-term Psychological Reaction to Rape

6.1. Introduction

The change in the psychological reaction to rape during the first year after the trauma was described by Burgess and Holmstrom as a transition from an acute disorganization phase to a reorganization phase, which usually takes place two to three weeks after the attack (Burgess and Holmstrom, 1974). Atkeson and co-workers found that most depressive reactions and social adjustment reactions return to normal within four months of the assault, whereas fear and anxiety reactions are more longlasting (Atkeson et al., 1982). Frank and co-workers found that depressive symptoms disminished significantly within three months, after which there was no significant change (Frank and Stewart, 1984). Kilpatrick and co-workers found that the psychological reaction to rape changed within three months; there was a decrease in most distress measures. The anxiety and fear restrictions were more longlasting and differentiated victims from non-victims for as long as three years after the assault (Kilpatrick, 1985). These studies did not use specific measurements for post-traumatic stress reactions and all had a high drop-out ratio (see Chapter 1). The course of the reaction should therefore be looked into once more. For clinical purposes it is also of interest to look for variations in reaction patterns within the victim group. The questions which will be raised in this chapter therefore are:

(1) Do the results from the present study confirm that a major change in the psychological reaction to rape most usually happens within three months?
(2) If a major change most usually takes place within three months, does this concern all subjects or are there different patterns within the victim group in the reaction to rape over time?

6.2. Method

Data from all three assessments are used in relation to the results presented here. This includes four self-assessment instruments 1. IES (Impact of Event Scale), 2. STAI x-1 (State Anxiety 12 items), 3. STAGI (State Aggression 6 items) and 4. GHQ-20, all used in the acute phase, at three months and after a year (13–16 months). The psychophysiological stress symptoms recorded on the Leymann stress-symptom list (SSL) will also be looked into. The ratings from the extended Comprehensive Psychopathological Rating-Scale (CPRS–PTSD) with its two subscales of ten items, one for post-traumatic stress symptoms PTSS and one for depression (MADRS), are also included in the presentation. The CPRS–PTSD scores are drawn from the semi-structured clinical interviews in the acute phase and after 13–16 months. For further description of the instruments see Chapter 3.

In addition, questions from the last interview regarding the participants' reports on duration of symptoms are used. In order to decide whether a difference in mean scores at two points in time was significant, a two-sided Wilcoxon rank-sum test was used.

6.3. Results

6.3.1. CHANGES IN REACTIONS/SYMPTOMS IN THE COURSE OF THE FIRST YEAR

Psychological reactions were measured on the self-assessment scales at three points in time:

6.3.1.1. Impact of Event Scale

Whereas the mean intrusion scores on the IES drop dramatically during the first three months, this is not so with the avoidance scores, where the change during the first three months is minimal (see Table 6.1).

The change in mean scores demonstrates the general tendency. The distribution at different levels of distress supplements the figures (see Table 6.2).

Both tables demonstrate the different course of intrusion and avoidance reactions: the decrease in avoidance is less and comes after three months. Whereas the majority have a drop in intrusion scores, about one-third remain unchanged and in two cases the intrusion score increases during the first three months. In nearly 50 percent of cases the avoidance reactions remain unchanged, whereas for the rest avoidance either increases or decreases.

The change over the next 10–12 months shows a slightly different pattern: avoidance drops most, either in combination with a drop in intrusion, or more often combined with unchanged intrusion. An increase in both intrusion and avoidance is seen in two cases.

6.3.1.2. State Anxiety and Aggression

The general tendency is a considerable decrease in anxiety from the first to the second assessment at three months. The drop in state anxiety was significantly related to drop in intrusion scores ($p < 0.001$), but not to decrease in avoidance scores. Unchanged anxiety level was found in nine cases and an increase in anxiety scores in five cases during the first three months.

Aggressive reactions in the acute phase were not frequent and the intensity was lower than one would expect. Nevertheless, over the first three months the decrease in aggressive feelings was statistically significant.

One can state conclusively that *the major change in intrusive symptoms and state anxiety happens in the first three months in the majority of the victims.* Aggressive reactions also decrease. The avoidance symptoms show a different pattern, with a decrease in intensity coming later, after the first three months. However, it is also clear that some victims diverge from the general pattern: reactions in some may show little change; the decrease may come later; or sometimes an inverse reaction appears.

6.3.1.3. General Health Questionnaire

The GHQ-20 in the first assessment is concerned with the two weeks prior to the assault and the results are therefore not directly

Table 6.1 *Mean intrusion and avoidance subscale scores on the IES in the acute phase, at 3 months and at 13–16 months post-assault*

IES	Acute phase		3 months		13–16 months
	Mean (SD)	p-value	Mean (SD)	p-value	Mean (SD)
Intrusion subscale score	N = 50 25.2 (7.6)	$p < 0.001$	N = 47 15.7 (9.5)	$p = 0.06$ n.s.	N=47 14.0 (8.6)
Avoidance subscale score	N = 47 21.6 (6.7)	n.s.	N = 47 21.0 (9.0)	$p = 0.01$	N = 47 18.1 (9.0)

Table 6.2 *Distribution of Impact of Event subscale scores at different levels of distress in the acute phase, at 3 months and 13–16 months post-assault*

Levels of distress	Acute phase No. (%)	3 months No. (%)	13–16 months No. (%)
Intrusion subscale score:	N=50	N=47	N=47
Low (<10)	2 (2)	16 (34)	16 (34)
Medium (10–19)	10 (22)	15 (32)	17 (36)
High (>19)	38 (76)	16 (34)	14 (30)
Avoidance subscale score:	N=47	N=47	N=47
Low (<10)	0 (0)	5 (11)	9 (19)
Medium (10–19)	21 (45)	16 (34)	13 (32)
High (>19)	26 (55)	26 (55)	23 (49)

Table 6.3 *Changes in state anxiety and state aggression scores measured by mean sum-scores in the acute phase at 3 months and at 13–16 months post-assault*

	Acute phase Mean (SD)	p-value	3 months Mean (SD)	p-value	13–16 months Mean (SD)
STAI x-1 range 12–48	N=50 36.0 (7)	$p < .001$	N=47 27.0 (9.7)	n.s.	N=47 29.0 (8.6)
Aggression:	N=47		N=47		N=47
STAGI range 6–24	13.0 (5)	$p = 0.001$	11.0 (4.1)	n.s.	10.1 (4.6)

comparable with the other measurements. The results at three months and 13–16 months are shown in Table 6.4.

6.3.1.4. Psychophysiological Symptoms

As expected, the decrease in psychophysiological symptoms between the first and the second assessment was considerable. The

Table 6.4 *General Health Questionnaire score at 3 months and at 13–16 months post-assault*

GHQ score	3 months No. (%)	p-value	13–16 months No. (%)
< 5	22 (46)		25 (53)
> 4	26 (54)		22 (47)
Mean score (SD)	7.5 (7.6)		6.0 (6.4)
		$p = 0.08$ n.s.	

N = 47

most frequent symptoms in the acute phase – nausea and muscle-ache, reported by 75 percent – were also among the frequent symptoms after three months, reported as occurring often or all the time by 19 percent (nausea) and 25 percent (muscle-ache). Stomach-ache (21 percent) and headache (23 percent) were also frequently reported symptoms.

The report on psychophysiological symptoms after a year did not differ essentially from the three-month assessment.

6.3.1.5. Change in Interview-based Psychopathological Scores from the First to the Last Assessment

Post-traumatic stress symptoms (PTSS). Table 6.5 demonstrates the decrease in post-traumatic stress reactions/symptoms from the acute phase to the follow-up assessment. The most frequent post-traumatic stress symptoms one year after the assault were hyper-vigilance, trauma avoidance and exaggerated startle response.

Depression sum-score (MADRS). The significant change in Table 6.6 demonstrates how *a depressive reaction is a main problem in the acute phase, but not after a year, when 25 percent stay moderately to severely depressed.*

Five participants reported that they had attempted suicide in the course of the first year. One of them judged the attempt to have nothing to do with her attempted rape experience. The other four had pre-rape mental problems, two had childhood histories of physical and sexual abuse and had attempted suicide before. After the rape, all of them developed considerable rape-related symptoms in addition to their former problems.

Table 6.5 *Change in mean sum-scores of PTSS and in distribution of scores from the first to the last assessment post-assault*

| | Acute phase | | 13–16 months | | |
	Mean	(SD)	Mean	(SD)	p-value
PTSS sum-score	30.0	(9.2)	23.0	(9.2)	p < 0.001
Distribution of sum-score:	No.	%	No.	%	
<10	0	0	3	6.4	
10–19	8	15.1	12	25.5	
20–29	18	34.0	20	42.6	
>30	27	50.9	12	25.5	

N = 47

Table 6.6 *Change in depressive sum-scores (MADRS) from the acute phase to one year post-assault*

| | Acute phase | | 13–16 months | | Significance |
	Mean	(SD)	Mean	(SD)	of difference
MADRS sum-score	27.4	(10.0)	12.0	(8.3)	p < 0.001)
Distribution of sum-score	*No.*	%	*No.*	%	
0–6 (no depression)	0	0	14	30	
7–19 (mild)	11	21	21	45	
20–34 (moderate)	30	57	11	23	
>34 (severe)	12	22	1	2	

N = 47

The major change in post-traumatic stress reactions as well as in depressive reactions is a considerable decrease in symptom level, but the decrease is much more prominent for depressive symptoms. However, looking at the change for each participant, we can see that they do *not all follow the major reaction pattern.*

Differences within the victim group. Two main patterns emerge as regards change in post-traumatic stress symptoms scored on CPRS–PTSD:

Group 1 (N = 18) show either (a) a worse outcome with an increase in symptoms of more than 4 (N = 7), or (b) almost unchanged scores (plus/minus 4) (N = 11). Eight of the participants in this group also show unchanged or increased depressive sum-scores. The self-assessment scores for this group either increase or remain unchanged.

Group 2 (N = 29) show a clear decrease in scores, either (a) small (5–9) (N = 8) or (b) considerable (>10) (N = 21). All participants in this group also show an significant decrease in depressive scores and in self-assessment scores. However, about 10 participants who had very high scores on all assessments in the acute phase still have high scores after a year, although there has been a decrease in their scores.

6.3.2. SELF-REPORTED DURATION OF SYMPTOMS

In the follow-up interview after one year the participants judged the duration of post-rape reactions/symptoms. Table 6.7 shows that the

Table 6.7 *Self-reported duration of reactions/symptoms that had developed after the rape, 1 year post-assault*

Duration	No.	%
< 1 month	0	0
1–3 months	3	6
3–6 months	5	11
6–12 months	6	13
>12 months	29	62
Uncertain	4	8

N = 47

majority of victims (62 percent) report that they are still bothered by reactions/symptoms one year after the rape. Data from the self-assessment scores do not fully explain why some victims feel recovered after three months, six months or a year. Only interview data and scores from the CRPS–PTSD interview explain this. Post-traumatic stress symptoms for many victims do not occur as chronic problems, in the sense that they are present all the time. The reactions might represent problems that a person knows can be triggered by exposure to certain stimuli. The following example illustrates why a victim does not consider herself fully recovered, although at the time of the last assessment she had minimal reactions and low self-assessment scores.

No. 21 was assaulted walking on her way home late one evening. She was threatened with a knife, taken into a wood and raped. Her self-assessment scores show a relatively high state anxiety (34) in the acute phase, which drops remarkably in the first three months (to 18) and then remains the same. She has low intrusion scores on all assessments, moderate avoidance scores at first, which drop and then increase a bit but remain low (14–0–7) on the self assessment. Interview scores on post-traumatic stress symptoms give a moderate sum-score in the acute phase and remain the same at the one-year follow-up (20). Her main symptoms at the follow-up are infrequent and moderate traumatophobia, some concentration difficulties, exaggerated startle response and hypervigilance. Her depression score drops from moderate to low from the first to the last assessment. Her GHQ score at 3 months and 13–16 is 0. Her main problem after the rape was fear of being alone indoors, and of walking alone outdoors, fear of the area where the rape took place, and fear of knives. She did not define the hypervigilance as a problem, although it was unpleasant, but as necessary in order to protect herself. She took driving lessons and got herself a driving licence and a second-hand car to avoid having to walk alone outdoors, especially at night. She and her husband moved from the area and she changed her job. At the last assessment she reports that the fear of being alone at home subsided after some weeks, but could still occur, although very seldom. In the first six months her fear of being alone outdoors was constant, but at the time of the last follow-up interview she seldom has this fear, and most of the time she feels OK. However, she does not go out alone after dark and does not consider herself recovered as long as she knows that her fear can be activated.

6.4. Discussion

The present results confirm that for the majority of victims there seems to be a decrease in distress measures such as intrusive re-experiencing and state anxiety during the first three months. Aggressive reactions also diminish. The psychophysiological stress symptoms, which are intense in the first days, are, as might be expected, radically changed after three months and then remain unchanged. The intensity of these reactions is most of all a phenomenon of the acute phase. Trauma-avoidance reactions, however, do not decrease so fast; the decrease occurs mainly after three months and is less impressive than for the other scores. A decrease in anxiety, aggression and intrusion, but not in avoidance, could make victims of rape less interested in treatment after the first few months, even when their avoidance reactions give them functional difficulties. Another possibility is that they will make more effort to avoid the topic of the rape in a treatment situation after the first few months, not because it is no longer relevant, but out of fear of triggering the anxiety-provoking re-experiences which are now kept under control.

In the present study, there is no specific self-report measurement for depressive reactions, although the GHQ does cover some depressive symptoms. However, since the participants were asked to fill out pre-rape functioning on the first GHQ, the changes in the first three months are missing. The interview scores show that the change in depressive scores from the acute phase to one year post-assault is impressive and more significant than any other decrease.

The decrease in post-traumatic stress symptoms from the first to the last assessment is not so dramatic, but nevertheless significant. Since this sum-score has not been used before (although the post-traumatic stress symptoms have been added and used in other studies), levels for low, moderate and severe distress have not been worked out. It is also debatable whether this would be useful. Some post-traumatic stress symptoms are highly specific, such as involuntary re-experiencing or trauma-avoidance. Others, like loss of interest or concentration difficulties, are specific only when they appear together with the specific symptoms. It would clearly be possible, for instance, to meet the diagnostic criteria for PTSD with a relatively low sum-score (e.g. <20) if the composition of symptoms were right. Here the sum-scores are used mainly as an instrument to describe a change in levels of post-traumatic stress symptoms in the course of the first year. However, not all victims react in the same way, and, whereas a majority improve over time, a group of victims can worsen or do not get better. There is, of course, a possibility that these victims more than the others have been caught in a bad phase at each assessment. Post-traumatic stress reactions are phasic and non-stable. Another possibility is that the participants were distressed before the rape, and that an increase or no change reflects a chronic condition. The information from the first assessment on pre-rape functioning and post-traumatic stress symptoms does not confirm this. Some of those with pre-rape mental problems showed a marked decrease in their post-traumatic stress symptom scores after the acute phase. Only one who increased her scores had mental problems in the year before the rape and they were of a different nature. However, in the next two chapters the sample will be examined more thoroughly for mental health disorders that have developed since the rape and the predictive factors for these. The results on coping will also indicate how coping strategy is related to outcome.

6.5. Conclusion

The results presented here confirm that, for the majority of victims, the most significant decrease in symptoms usually happens within the first three months. Avoidance reactions, however, do not follow this pattern; the decrease comes later and is less prominent. This tendency is general and the clinician should be aware of it as it might be a reason for victims of rape dropping treatment or avoiding the topic of their rape experience in the treatment. The present study also reveals that a group of victims either do not change or get worse in the course of the first year. The search for predictors as well as differences in coping strategies, which will be presented later, might give some answers to why some improve and others do not.

7

Mental Health Problems in Victims of Rape One Year After the Assault

7.1. Introduction

Research on long-term psychological reactions in victims of rape has been going on for 20 years. The picture of victims' reactions has been relatively consistent, describing fears, phobias, nightmares, depression, sexual problems, and social adjustment problems (Burgess and Holmstrom, 1974; Nadelson et al., 1982; Ellis, 1983). Several investigators have pointed out that many of the symptoms found in rape victims are consistent with the symptoms of Post-Traumatic Stress Disorder (Burgess and Holstrom, 1985; Nadelson et al., 1982; Kilpatrick et al., 1985). However, the presence of the clinical disorder as a long-term consequence of rape has not been documented. The presence of post-traumatic stress reactions or symptoms is not enough to meet the criteria for the clinical diagnosis; the presence of all criteria symptoms as well as the frequency and intensity of the different symptoms have to be taken into account (DSM-III-R, 1987).

The aim of this chapter is therefore to address the following questions:

(1) Do victims of rape develop long-term mental health problems after the assault?
(2) Do victims of rape develop *long-term* post-traumatic stress symptoms and/or Post-Traumatic Stress Disorder (PTSD)?
(3) If the victims do develop long-term PTSD, what is the co-morbidity with other rape-related disorders?

7.2. Method

The results presented here come from the first assessment in the acute phase and the reassessment after one year of 47 women from the original group of 53 (89 percent). The data from the first assessment relevant for this chapter are the data on pre-rape mental health problems. In the reassessment at 13–16 months after the rape I examined the present state of the participant and decided whether she had developed problems *after the rape* that met the criteria for a DSM-III-R diagnosis.

The standardized measurements relevant for the results here are the self-rating scales IES, STAI x-1, STAGI, GHQ, the interview-based CPRS–PTSD (the extended Comprehensive Psychopathological Rating Scale) with subscales for depression (MADRS) and post-traumatic stress symptoms (PTS). A list of 14 rape-related fears from Veronen and Kilpatrick's Modified Fear Survey were also included in the interview (Resick et al., 1986). The subjects were asked to estimate the intensity of the fears on a seven-point ordinal scale, both when the fears had been most intense and how they had been during the previous two weeks. The list also served as a basis for interviewing about fears that had developed after the rape, and explanations and other items were written down.

For additional information not available on CPRS–PTSD (e.g. sexual problems, substance-abuse problems), SCID (Structural Clinical Interview for DSM-III) was used (Spitzer and Williams, 1984). The DSM-III diagnosis was given after the assessment and later revised to be in accordance with DSM-III-R. The symptom scores from the CPRS–PTSD formed the basis for the diagnostic procedure, but other interview data relating to functioning, the duration of symptoms and the nature of specific fears were taken into account. The researcher also used SCID as a guide to see whether all criteria were met. If the participants presented symptoms already reported in the first assessment as pre-rape mental problems, these were not diagnosed, but labelled unchanged, as the problems developing after the rape were those of interest.

Reliability. Eighteen participants allowed the last CPRS-interview to be taped, and these interviews were later scored by another psychiatrist. Cohen's kappa was used as measure of reliability. Before assessing inter-rate reliability, the CPRS was reduced to the original three-point scale created by Åsberg (0–1, 2–3, 4–6). This procedure allowed the estimation of reliability for each item with kappa statistics based on 18 participants. The kappa coefficient for each item varied between 0.43 (hostile feelings) and 1.00 (sadness) with a mean of 0.73.

In order to decide whether a mean difference between two groups was statistically significant a two-sided Wilcoxon rank sum-test was used.

Table 7.1 *New diagnostic categories (DSM-III-R axis 1) found in victims of rape one year post-assault*

Main diagnosis	No.
PTSD	14
Simple (sexual) phobia	6
Female sexual arousal disorder	10
Major depressive disorder	6
Social phobia	1

N = 23

7.3. Mental Disorders One Year Post-Assault

Of the 47 women who participated in the follow-up assessment, 23 (49 percent) had new problems that had developed after the rape event and met the criteria for a DSM-III-R diagnosis. The new diagnostic categories which were present were PTSD, simple (sexual) phobia, female sexual arousal disorder, major depressive disorder and social phobia (see Table 7.1).

Although some increased their use of alcohol in the first months post-assault, no one developed long-term alcohol or drug-abuse problems after the rape. Nine women had substance-abuse problems before the rape – one dropped out of the study, two had increased their abuse of alcohol, three had improved and the rest remained unchanged.

To demonstrate the difference between the diagnostic and non-diagnostic group, the symptom scores from the self-rating instruments and the CPRS post-traumatic stress (PTS) and depressive (MADRS) subscales are shown in Table 7.2. As the table demonstrates, the difference between the diagnostic and non-diagnostic group is highly significant for all scales, but is least for the IES avoidance subscale.

7.3.1. POST-TRAUMATIC STRESS SYMPTOMS AND PTSD

Fourteen women (30 percent) had developed PTSD. Moderate post-traumatic stress symptoms or reactions were seen in an additional 13 women (28 percent).

The distribution of post-traumatic stress symptoms in the PTSD group, the moderate post-traumatic stress reaction group, and the mild/no symptom group is shown in Table 7.3. As the table clearly demonstrates, re-experiencing, trauma-avoidance, hypervigilance

Table 7.2 *The distribution of mean scores on the STAI x-1, STAGI, IES intrusion subscale, IES avoidance subscale, GHQ, CPRS − PTS subscale and CPRS subscale for depression (MADRS) in the diagnostic and non-diagnostic groups one year post assault*

Instrument	Diagnostic group N=23 Mean score	(SD)	Non-diagnostic group N=24 Mean score	(SD)	p-value
STAI x-1 (12 items)	34.0	(7.8)	24.1	(6.4)	p < 0.001
STAGI (6 items)	11.8	(4.8)	8.3	(3.7)	p < 0.01
IES intrusion	19.0	(8.2)	9.1	(5.9)	p < 0.001
IES avoidance	21.3	(8.3)	15.1	(8.7)	p < 0.05
GHQ	8.9	(6.7)	3.2	(4.7)	p < 0.01
CPRS–PTS	28.0	(8.6)	17.7	(6.7)	p < 0.001
CPRS–MADRS	17.3	(8.1)	8.5	(6.0)	p < 0.001

and exaggerated startle response were the most frequent symptoms in all three groups, although intensity and frequency vary.

Trauma-avoidance means typically phobic reactions to anything connected with the memory of the trauma and thus individually formulated. Many fears were unavoidable – e.g. seeing a man with a particular look, a foreigner, newspaper headlines concerning rape, physical contact – and could trigger the re-experiencing. Generalization of fear was usually connected with situations where the woman felt vulnerable to assault, such as darkness, people behind

Table 7.3 *Intensity of post-traumatic stress symptoms in the PTSD group, the moderate post-traumatic stress reaction group and the mild/no post-traumatic stress reaction group measured by CPRS − PTSD one year post-assault*

CPRS–PTSD item	PTSD N=14 Mean score	Moderate PTS reaction N=13 Mean score	Mild/no PTS reaction N=20 Mean score
Intrusive re-experiencing	3.9	2.2	1.5
Nightmares	2.9	0.9	0.4
Loss of interest	2.0	0.6	0.4
Estrangement/withdrawal	2.6	1.9	0.8
Trauma-avoidance	4.1	3.3	2.0
Reduced sleep	2.4	0.8	0.7
Irritability	3.0	2.0	1.5
Difficulty concentrating	3.1	2.2	1.5
Hypervigilance	4.2	2.8	2.4
Exaggerated startle response	4.2	3.9	2.4

one's back, walking alone in deserted areas, sudden noises, being touched by someone unexpectedly, crowds or queues where involuntary bumping into others was unavoidable.

Case example of PTSD

No. 16 was a 23-year-old woman with no earlier health problems. She worked as an assistant in a library and lived with her husband. She was assaulted on the street by two men who removed her forcibly to a dark room which they locked, and there she was raped.

She arrived at the Emergency Ward three days later asking for a medical examination. She was at the time of the first assessment very depressed, self-blaming, frightened and felt her life had been ruined. She could not sleep, suffered from intense flashbacks, feared men and physical contact. She did not want therapeutic help, explaining that she thought the best thing would be to pretend it had not happened and to get her husband to respect physical distance until it was all forgotten. At the follow-up she appeared tense and immediately said she had no problems. During the interview another picture emerged. She still lived with her husband, but they had had no sexual contact for the last six months. She still had her job at the library, but worked alone and hardly communicated with her work-mates. Although she had concentration difficulties, "it helped to have something to do". A number of stimuli triggered re-experiencing and she had restricted her life considerably to avoid such stimuli. This included not going out alone after dark, avoiding men, avoiding physical contact and avoiding other people in case they should start talking about unpleasant things like sex, assault, etc. She still had difficulties falling asleep, and intrusive thoughts about the rape appeared nearly every night, but she desperately rejected these thoughts and tried to think about something else. She had nightmares every week about men who wanted to kill her. When she was asked about physical symptoms, she said that she was bothered with breathing difficulties when she lay down, a feeling of suffocating, "as if a bad spirit sucks the air out of me". She did not relate this to the rape and did not remember the suffocating feeling she had described in the first interview about the rape, in relation to being kissed with the offender's hand squeezing her throat. She frequently used a mild drug against muscular pain.

Table 7.4 *Level of depression measured by MADRS one year post-assault*

MADRS score	Not depressed 0–9	Mild depression 10–19	Moderate/severe depression 20–
No.	19	16	12

N = 47

7.3.2. DEPRESSIVE SYMPTOMS AND DEPRESSIVE DISORDERS

Whereas the mean MADRS score in the first assessment was 27.4, the mean score one year post-rape was 12.8, which indicates the considerable change in the degree of depression from the acute phase to the follow-up. Twelve women (26 percent) were found to have moderate to severe depressive symptoms in the follow-up, indicated by MADRS scores above 19. The distribution of depression scores is shown in Table 7.4. Of the 12 depressed women, six had reported depressive symptoms before the rape and were categorized as not changed regarding depression. The other six women met criteria for a moderate major depressive disorder.

Case example of a major depressive disorder

No. 49 was a 19-year-old woman, with no psychiatric history, but with a history of diabetes since she was 13. She worked as a ward attendant in a hospital ward and lived with her parents. She had had a steady boyfriend for the last five months. She was raped by a man she knew by sight who offered her a lift. She came to the Emergency Ward some hours later accompanied by a friend and the police. At the first assessment she seemed very anxious, depressed, cried a lot and had suicidal thoughts, felt life made no sense. She feared that the offender would come back as he had threatened to do. She also felt ashamed, "it feels like everybody looks at me and can see what has happened." She did not dare to be alone, was bothered by flashbacks of the experience and had intense psychophysiological reactions like shivering, vomiting, sweating and palpitations. Her boyfriend broke off their relationship because she did not want to be touched. She got some therapeutic help in the first three months, managed to keep up her job and seemed to improve. At the time of the follow-up she had lost her job, she now lived with a new boyfriend and his family. She feared being alone, and claimed that her new boyfriend liked to protect her and she felt she needed a man to protect her. She was not bothered by nightmares, but re-experiencing symptoms could sometimes be triggered by sexual contact. She also suffered from inhibited sexual arousal and hypoactive sexual desire. She had lost interest in work and the activities she had shared with her friends. She was often bothered by stomach-ache and headache. Her diabetes was very unstable, she had lost her appetite and did not take the necessary measures to keep her disease under control. She slept poorly, felt chronically sad, had pessimistic and often suicidal thoughts, felt helpless and worthless. She knew she was taking risks with her health, but did not mind.

7.3.3. SEXUAL DISORDERS

Fourteen women (30 percent) were found to have developed sexual problems after the rape. Another five had reported sexual problems before the rape and were characterized as unchanged as regards sexual functioning. In terms of the diversity of sexual problems, two main groups emerged.

The first group of six women had developed **phobia of intercourse** and avoided sexual contact. They met the diagnostic criteria of a simple phobia rather than sexual aversion, since fear of sex, not aversion seemed to be the main problem. However, since their phobia was linked specifically to sexual intercourse, the disorder is listed as a sexual disorder.

Two of them had tried sexual contact, but had great difficulties in carrying it through and experienced flashbacks and sexual arousal problems. One of them also experienced dyspareunia. Sexual desire could be intact as long as sexual encounters were avoided, but half of them also reported a decrease in general desire for sex.

Case example of sex phobia

No. 11 was a 25-year-old divorced woman living with her 5-year-old daughter. She received single mothers' benefits and worked part time in an office. She was raped when she and another girl stayed the night at some friends' house. The two of them arrived at the Emergency Ward the next day.

She had been raped before, at the age of 15, but had never told anybody about it. In the acute phase she had very strong bodily reactions, felt depersonalized and had strong suicidal impulses.

She quickly pulled herself together when her daughter fell ill, and said it was impossible for her for practical reasons to receive therapeutic help. She was encouraged to use her network and received some support from both her mother and a couple of friends. She was unable to work for months after the rape, felt very depressed and was troubled by muscular tensions and pelvic infections. At the follow-up her main problem was fear of sexual intercourse. She had about eight months previously fallen in love with a man who also cared for her. However, even though she had sexual feelings for him, she panicked every time they tried to have intercourse. This had become so difficult that after six months they broke off the relationship. She felt extremely sad about it and thought the chances of ever having a normal relationship with a man to be zero.

The second group of 10 women were characterized by **sexual arousal problems** with inhibition of a sexual arousal response including physiological manifestations. They met the diagnostic criteria for female sexual arousal disorder. These problems appeared in sexual encounters in which the woman from previous experience expected arousal, e.g. when being in love and/or being attracted to a male partner. However, this group did not just present inhibition of sexual arousal; five of them also reported hypoactive sexual desire and three of them dyspareunia. As noted above, two of them also had a phobia of sexual intercourse.

Case example of sexual arousal disorder

No. 7 was a 28-year-old switchboard operator who shared a flat with two friends. She was raped by a superficial acquaintance on her way home late one evening. She arrived at the Emergency Ward alone the same night. Her immediate reaction was emotional; she cried and shivered, felt extremely upset, dirty and frightened. She received therapeutic help for about three months and worked actively to overcome her fears. The post-traumatic stress symptoms like sleep disturbances, nightmares and intrusive re-experiencing diminished considerably during this process. At the follow-up she was still bothered sometimes with nightmares and flashbacks, mostly triggered by newspaper headlines about rape or violence, but felt she could cope with the symptoms, which did not appear very often. She had a boyfriend at the time of the rape, but he broke off the relationship shortly afterwards.

Her explanation for this was that their sex life changed radically as she lost interest in sex and did not get aroused as she used to. She had tried to engage in a relationship with a man a couple of months before the follow-up, but felt she was still not interested in sex and did not get aroused when she expected to be. She felt she had changed and matured after the rape and was satisfied with the ways she had managed to cope with her fears, but in the sexual area she was as dysfuctional as she had been directly after the rape.

Two women who reported satisfaction with their sexual relations in stable partnerships, when asked specifically, answered that they had developed intromission dysparaneuia (pain connected to being penetrated). However, the pain usually subsided quickly and they were able to enjoy sex and did not feel this symptom made it difficult to function sexually. They were therefore excluded from the sexual problems group.

7.3.4. SOCIAL PHOBIA

One woman met the diagnostic criteria for a social phobia at the time of the follow-up interview.

Her case history was in many aspects different, in the sense that her major problems developed after six months, when she was informed about the date of the court case. Until then she had been extremely avoidant and denied any problems, although the rape was extremely brutal and her acute shock reaction severe, being also complicated by head injury. When testifying in court she denied having had any mental problems, although she had given up work after a long period of changing jobs because she feared her work-mates. She also knew that she would get much higher compensation if the court decided that the experience had been damaging to her health. After the court case, she became suicidal and was overwhelmed by intrusive symptoms. She asked for therapeutic help, but said she could only work through her experience in a safe place and asked to be admitted to a psychiatric hospital. At the time of the follow-up she was still in hospital, but much less anxious. She had moderate post-traumatic stress symptoms, but did not meet the diagnostic criteria for a PTSD diagnosis as she no longer had involuntary re-experiences. However, the social phobia was still a major problem. Her fear was related to being asked anything personal and thereby not being able to conceal her rape experience.

7.3.5. RELATION BETWEEN PTSD, SEXUAL DISORDERS AND DEPRESSION

Of the 14 PTSD patients, eight had high depression scores (MADRS > 19). Four of them had been depressed and had sexual problems before the rape, three of them living in abusive relationships. These problems were labelled unchanged and have not been included in Figure 7.1, which demonstrates the interrelation between the post-rape mental health problems.

Six of the 14 women who reported sexual problems that had developed after the rape event also met the criteria of a PTSD diagnosis. Another six had sexual problems as their main problem, four of these belonging to the moderate PTSD group. An additional two from the sexual problem group also had a major depressive disorder, one a sexual phobia, the other an arousal disorder, which was sometimes also complicated by post-traumatic re-experiencing during intercourse. Their sexual problems seemed to have a more post-traumatic stress nature than one would expect as a result of depression in itself.

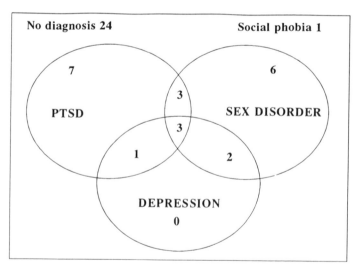

Figure 7.1 *The interrelation of post-rape mental problems in 23 women who met the criteria for a DSM-III-R diagnosis one year post-assault (N=47)*

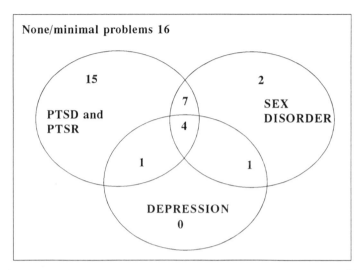

Figure 7.2 *The interrelation of a moderate post-traumatic reaction (PTSR), PTSD, sexual problems and depression one year post-assault (N=47)*

If the moderate post-traumatic stress reaction group is included in the figure, the overlapping is as demonstrated in Figure 7.2. The diagram shows that, when the moderate post-traumatic stress symptom/reaction group is added to the PTSD group, the overlapping with sexual problems and depression increases somewhat, although the main increase is within the post-traumatic stress symptom group.

The seven women in the **worst outcome group** (increase of symptoms in the course of the first year – see chapter 6) all belonged to the DSM-III-R diagnostic group; five had developed PTSD, one social phobia and one sexual disorders (sexual phobia and female sexual arousal disorder).

7.4. Discussion

The present results demonstrate that post-traumatic stress symptoms such as re-experiencing, trauma-avoidance, hypervigilance and exaggerated startle response were also frequent among the women who did not meet the criteria for a DSM-III-R diagnosis. The presence of post-traumatic stress symptoms in a range from mild to intense reactions demonstrates that after-effects are a question not of either/or, but of their degree and influence on functioning. The significant difference in all standardized measures between the diagnostic and non-diagnostic group does, however, demonstrate that the diagnostic group is a far more troubled group than the other participants and therefore is of special interest for clinical practice.

The sexual disorders, which were as frequent as PTSD, had a phobic or response-inhibitory nature. These symptoms can be looked upon as part of a trauma-avoidance symptomatology when they appear within the PTSD group. Sexual problems alone might present a less complicated reaction to rape or they might represent a PTSD sequela. Orgasmic sexual dysfunctions were not explored in the present study. The main reason for this was that orgasmic dysfunction was not considered a serious disadvantage in relation to being able to function sexually. Also many of the participants were young with limited sexual experience and reported that they had found sex pleasurable although they had not experienced orgasm yet. Thus only the disorders that had a serious impact on functioning were picked out.

In the one case of social phobia, the symptomatology was rape related and her phobia could also be regarded as a PTSD sequela. Her history indicated that she would have met the criteria of PTSD when she was admitted to hospital, where they also diagnosed her as suffering from PTSD. That she was without the re-experiencing symptoms at the reassessment could be a result of the therapeutic help she had received or a result of living in a protected environment.

Long-lasting depressive symptoms were not a major problem for the majority of the victims. Only six (13 percent) who had not reported depressive symptoms before the rape were found to have a moderate/severe level of depression after a year. In the present sample, depression did not appear alone, but was combined with sexual problems or PTSD. Some depressive symptoms will to a certain extent resemble some of the numbing symptoms in PTSD, e.g. loss of interest, difficulty concentrating, reduced sleep, but the range of depressive symptoms went beyond those. Also, the degree of depression varied a great deal within the PTSD group. This raises the question whether there are specific factors that contribute to a depressive development.

According to the DSM-III and DSM-III-R, sexual problems are not to be diagnosed when they appear within a depressive disorder.

It can be debated whether or not the sexual problems the participants suffered from were a result of depression. It is just as likely
that they represent independent post-traumatic symptoms in addition to the depression, or that the depression is a consequence of the
loss of pleasure and ability to function sexually.
Four women in the PTSD group had previous sexual problems
and were also depressed before the rape. They were all traumatized
before, and three of them lived in abusive relationships before the
rape. According to both the material from the first assessment and
information from other doctors, they did not have a PTSD before
the rape. It is, however, possible that the severe long-term PTSD
was triggered by the rape experience but rooted in the former
traumatization. Earlier longitudinal studies of long-term reactions
to rape have not looked specifically at PTSD, or at the relationship
between the different symptom groups. Fear and anxiety reactions
have been reported as being most specific after one year post-
assault (Calhoun et al., 1982; Kilpatrick et al., 1981). It is reason-
able to consider that the post-traumatic stress symptoms and
reactions found in the present study partly reflect the same phenomena. Concerning depression, Atkeson and co-workers found that,
although most victims return to a normal level after 4 months, a
small number of victims continue to exhibit depressive symptoms at
4, 8 and 12 months post-assault (Atkeson et al., 1982). This is in
accordance with the present findings, which indicate that a smaller
group remains depressed.
    Burgess and Holmstrom have described sexual problems after
rape as characterized by changes in frequency of sexual activity and
in sexual responses (Burgess and Holmstrom, 1979). Becker and
co-workers, who categorized the sexual dysfunctions in a study
comparing rape victims, incest victims and normal controls, found
that the vast majority of sexual dysfunctions resulting from rape
were response-inhibitory problems such as fear of sex, arousal
dysfunction or desire dysfunction (Becker et al., 1982). This finding
is confirmed in the present study, even though the sample source
was completely different and their study was retrospective.
    The present findings demonstrate how individuals differ in their
recovery from rape. For clinical practice this raises an important
question about risk factors. Is it possible to identify patients at risk
in the acute phase? Do different factors contribute to different
problems? If this is the case, choice of treatment might be planned
more selectively at an early stage. These questions will be dealt with
in the next chapter.

7.5. Conclusion

The results in the present study of long-term mental health problems document long-term PTSD to be the main post-assault consequence for health. However, the results also demonstrate that post-traumatic stress reactions are frequent in a range from mild to severe, rather than being either/or. Sexual dysfunctions, which were as frequent as PTSD, can also be seen as symptoms of post-traumatic stress, e.g. physiological re-experiencing and phobic avoidance. Depression, however, can probably not be seen as a post-traumatic stress reaction, but represents an independent reaction.

The difference between the diagnostic and non-diagnostic group on all measures confirms the previous finding concerning differences within the victim group. An identification of disorders is meaningful only to the extent that it has therapeutic implications. The potential development of PTSD, sexual problems or depression will have to influence treatment strategy at an early stage if such a development is to be prevented. An investigation of predictors of the development of the different disorders that can be identified in the acute stage will therefore be presented in the next chapter.

8
Predictors of Long-term Psychiatric Outcome in Victims of Rape

8.1. Introduction

The purpose of identifying predictors of long-term psychiatric consequences of rape in a clinical context is to facilitate more effective treatment for victims at risk. Thus the main focus in this part of the study will be predictive factors that can be identified in the acute phase.

Several investigators have focused on predictive factors in relation to psychological distress after rape. In the follow-up study by Kilpatrick and co-workers this was done in relation to the degree of psychological distress three months after the assault. Their main findings suggest that the degree of initial distress is the best predictor of distress after three months (Kilpatrick et al., 1985). They argue that, since the reaction does not change significantly after three months, the same should be true of longer-term problems. In a retrospective study of crime-related PTSD, the same research group found that factors associated with a PTSD development in crime victims were completed rape, cognitive appraisal of life-threat and/or physical injury (Kilpatrick et al., 1989). The main problem with retrospective studies is that the retrospective memory construction may not be in accordance with what is actually presented in the acute phase. Other retrospective studies looking for predictors will therefore not be mentioned here.

In their longitudinal study, Atkeson and co-workers found that predictors of long-term depressive reactions were age, low socioeconomic status (older and poorer women were more at risk), assault reaction, prior psychiatric treatment history and physical health problems prior to the rape (Atkeson et al., 1982). Apart from the mentioned study on depression and Kilpatrick's retrospective study, studies of predictive factors in relation to a specific outcome such as a psychiatric diagnosis are lacking in the literature. In relation to treatment this might be of importance.

Two questions will therefore be raised in this chapter:

(1) Is it possible to identify factors in the acute phase that predict a long-term psychiatric outcome as described in the previous chapter?

(2) Are there specific predictive factors for PTSD, sexual dysfunctions and depressive reactions?

8.2. Method

Data from the first assessment are used to identify factors that might contribute to a psychiatric outcome (predictors). The data represent standardized measurements as well as quantitative categorization of qualitative interview data (see Chapter 3). The variables from the first assessment are divided into three groups:

(1) factors related to the assault;
(2) factors related to the person and their network;
(3) factors related to the acute response of the victim and her report on the responses from her network.

Indicators of long-term psychiatric outcome stem from the results presented in Chapter 7 concerning psychiatric disorders that have developed after the rape, as well as from the separate registration of PTSD, sexual disorders and depression. As depressive disorders were few in number, the indicator for depression used in the analyses was set to a score of >20 (moderate to severe) on the CPRS subscale for depression (MADRS), one year post-assault.

In order to decide whether an association between two binary variables − e.g. severe violence during assault (yes/no) and PTSD (yes/no) − was statistically significant, a two-sided exact Fisher–Irwin test was used. In order to decide whether a combination of predictors had significantly better "predictive power" than each of the predictors alone, logistic regression analysis was applied. A statistical tendency of association refers to p-values in the range 0.05–0.2.

Development of a predictive index. The aim of constructing a predictive index was to develop a method for identifying women with increased risk of a psychiatric outcome, and further to identify women with an increased risk of PTSD, sexual disorders and depressive reactions. Because of the relatively low number of subjects in this study, it was decided that the method should be based on at most three risk factors. The factors selected should be essentially distinct to avoid their covering the same phenomena. It should also be possible to identify the factors in an acute phase evaluation. Among these factors, the three with the strongest outcome association were selected.

8.3. Results

8.3.1. PREDICTORS OF LONG-TERM PSYCHIATRIC OUTCOME

For the whole psychiatric outcome group, the 23 women who met the criteria for a DSM-III-R diagnosis for problems that had developed after the rape event (see Chapter 7), only a few factors from the initial assessment proved to have predictive value.

8.3.1.1. Factors Related to the Assault

One assault variable, namely penetration ($p < 0.05$), proved to be a condition for long-term psychiatric outcome in this study.

8.3.1.2. Factors Related to Person/Network

Two person/network variables, namely low social support ($p < 0.05$) and negative relation to partner ($p < 0.05$), showed an association with a psychiatric outcome. Growing up in a home with a good atmosphere served as a protective factor ($p < 0.01$).

8.3.1.3. Factors Related to the Acute Response

One reaction variable, blame from network ($p < 0.05$), had a predictive value. The only individual acute reaction variable that indicated a tendency ($p = 0.10$) was the depression score.

8.3.1.4. A Predictive Index for a Psychiatric Outcome

Logistic regression showed that the combination of two variables, namely penetration and low social support, had a better "predictive power" than any other combination or any single predictor. This predictive index had a sensitivity of 65.5 percent, a specificity of 61 percent and a positive predictive power of 68 percent.

8.3.2. PREDICTORS OF POST-TRAUMATIC STRESS DISORDER (PTSD)

8.3.2.1. Factors Related to the Assault

Considerable physical violence (violence that went beyond use of restraint, physical strength or force) and experienced death threat

Table 8.1 *Relation between a PTSD outcome and variables connected with assault, person/network and the acute response*

Factors from initial assessment regarding assault, person/network and acute response	Relation to PTSD outcome
Considerable physical violence	$p < 0.05$
Experienced death threat	$p < 0.05$
Considerable physical violence and/or weapon (violence/threat factor)	$p < 0.01$
Functional impairment in the past due to psychiatric symptoms	$p < 0.02$
Received psychological/psychiatric treatment in the past	$p < 0.05$
Poor satisfaction in partner relationship	$p < 0.01$
Low social support	$p = 0.07$ n.s.
Sexual or violent traumatization <12 years of age	$p = 0.07$ n.s.
More than one abuse experience	$p = 0.06$ n.s.
Blame from close network	$p < 0.01$

were found to be statistically significant in their relation to PTSD outcome ($p < 0.05$ in both cases). If the factor "considerable physical violence" was combined with the factor "threat or use of weapon" into one "violence/threat" factor this factor proved highly significant ($p < 0.01$).

With a small sample, it is also tempting to see whether the tendencies of association form any pattern. Using the tendencies in this way one could cautiously say that a completed rape with a violent start by a stranger or partner who uses verbal threats and violence or weapons, and where the victim experiences a threat to her life, makes the victim susceptible towards developing PTSD (see Chapter 4, section 6.1, "The violent rape").

The effect of alcohol on the victim, whether she felt any warning signal, whether she resisted actively, and whether she used problem-solving strategies during the attack are factors that seem to have little significance for a PTSD development.

8.3.2.2. Factors Related to Person/Network

The most statistically significant relations were found between development of PTSD and a report of poor partner relationship ($p < 0.01$), psychiatric functional impairment in past history ($p < 0.05$), and to have been bothered by psychiatric symptoms in the six months prior to the rape ($p < 0.05$). To have received treatment for psychiatric problems was also predictive ($p < 0.05$).

Factors indicating a statistical tendency were also seen for low social support, sexual or violent traumatization before the age of 12 and more than one abuse experience. Some of these factors are interrelated. Women with earlier psychiatric complaints that had caused functional impairment (N = 12) also reported less social support, and were more likely to report having experienced abuse (violent or sexual) before the age of 12 (50 percent); 65 percent of these women had more than one abuse experience.

There is a tendency towards a better outcome in women who have higher education. Experiencing a high degree of social support also serves as a protective factor.

8.3.2.3. Factors Related to the Acute Psychological Reaction

Although the mean values on all reaction scores from the acute phase were higher in the PTSD group, the differences were not statistically significant. MADRS scores in the acute phase correlated at a level of $p = 0.05$, but picking out only the high scores (>25) gave no significance ($p = 0.18$). Level of intrusion in the acute phase was associated with post-traumatic stress symptoms after one year, but only if one added the moderate post-traumatic stress reaction/symptom group to the PTSD diagnostic group ($p < 0.05$). IES avoidance showed a tendency ($p = 0.09$) by mean scores, but isolating only scores above 20 gave no significance.

Neither anxiety level, aggression level, post-traumatic stress score, dissociation symptoms, shame, guilt, feelings of being damaged, nor amnesia in the acute phase were by presence or intensity significantly related with a PTSD outcome, although the mean values were slightly higher in the PTSD group.

Negative attitudes from others in the acute phase were more clearly related to a PTSD outcome. Being blamed by someone in the family and/or close network was associated with a PTSD outcome ($p < 0.01$).

Least likely to develop a PTSD were those who claimed that friends understood them and were their main supporters ($p < 0.05$). Supportive attitudes from police and health personnel showed a tendency to serve as protective factors.

8.3.2.4. A Predictive Index for PTSD

The combination of three independent predictive factors from each variable group gave a better predictive power than any single factor and/or any other combination of the factors that showed a significant relation to a PTSD outcome, namely: (1) the violence/threat

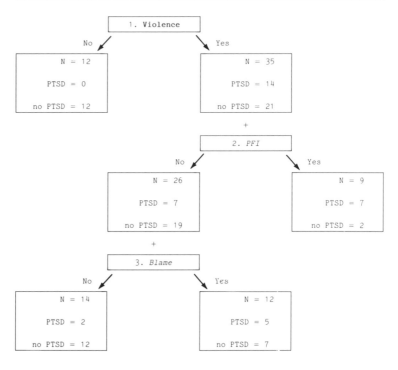

Figure 8.1 *The association between violence, psychiatric functional impairment in the past (PFI) and blame from close network as predictive factors for a PTSD outcome one year post-assault (N = 47)*

factor (considerable physical violence and/or weapon), (2) psychiatric functional impairment in the past (PFI), and (3) blame from family/close network.

The violence factor, factor 1, was a condition for a PTSD outcome; no one without such experience developed long-term PTSD (see Figure 8.1). This was also the case in the moderate posttraumatic stress reaction group (see Chapter 7) – with two exceptions, where only verbal threats of bodily harm were experienced. Factor 1 combined with Factor 2 resulted in a PTSD outcome in 78 percent of cases (7/9). Factor 1 with an absence of factor 2 resulted in a PTSD outcome in 27 percent (7/26). Logistic regression shows that, in addition to factor 1, both factors 2 and 3 contributed as predictors, but factor 2 was stronger. Factor 3 (blame) became an important additional factor when factor 2 was missing and resulted in a PTSD outcome in 42 percent (5/12), whereas only 14 percent (2/14) had a PTSD outcome related to factor 1 alone. The predictive index consisting of the three factors had a sensitivity of 86 percent, a specificity of 73 percent and a positive predictive power of 58 percent.

8.3.3. PREDICTORS OF SEXUAL DISORDERS

8.3.3.1. Factors Related to the Assault

No assault variables showed a statistically significant relation to a sexual disorder outcome. However, *no one who was not penetrated developed a sexual disorder*. Because of the small number of attempted rapes, this factor became significant only in relation to the whole psychiatric outcome group.

The statistical tendencies indicated that women who liked the offender before the rape, women who had not consumed alcohol, where the offender applied confidence-inducing strategies in the situation before and the prelude phase, where the offender used considerable physical violence or verbal threats or where the rape lasted more than an hour were more susceptible to develop a sexual disorder. The women who developed sexual disorders also had more difficulty in expressing what had been the worst aspect of the rape experience.

8.3.3.2. Factors Related to Person/Network

Only one factor was significantly related to sexual disorders, namely satisfaction with life before the rape; women who reported in the initial assessment that they had been well satisfied with their life before the rape were more likely to develop sexual disorders ($p < 0.05$).

The statistical tendencies indicated that women who were young (under 25 years) and healthy (with no serious physical or mental problems before the rape and no visits to a physician in the previous year) were more likely to develop a sexual disorder.

A high degree of experienced social support and high satisfaction with the partner relationship before the rape tended to serve as protective factors.

8.3.3.3. Factors Related to the Acute Response

Three acute response factors were significantly related to a sexual disorder outcome, namely a high CPRS depression sum-score of

MADRS >25 ($p < 0.01$), a depersonalization CPRS score of >3, ($p < 0.05$) and that the women reported that they felt damaged ($p < 0.01$) by the rape.

8.3.3.4. A Predictive Index for Sexual Disorders

A combination of two independent factors had a better predictive power than any single factor or any other combination, namely: (1) satisfied with life before the rape, and (2) a high degree of depression (MADRS score >25) in the acute phase. The combination of the two factors gave a sensitivity of 71 percent, a specificity of 82 percent and a positive predictive power of 71 percent.

8.3.4. PREDICTORS OF DEPRESSION

8.3.4.1. Factors Related to the Assault

Only one of the assault variables, namely more than one offender ($p < 0.05$), was significantly related to depression in victims at one year post-assault.

Statistical tendencies indicated that a social prelude to the rape, an offender one knows well, to have consumed more than one glass of beer/wine, verbal threats, to have obeyed orders from the offender and to have been forced to other sexual acts than vaginal penetration could be associated with long-term depression.

To have been assaulted by a stranger, to have resisted actively during the rape and to have used problem-solving strategies tended to serve as protective factors in relation to depression.

8.3.4.2. Factors Related to Person/Network

Three person/network variables were significantly related to depression, namely that the victim reported having been in a negative mood (irritable, sad) prior to the assault ($p < 0.05$), that the victim reported having experienced earlier violent or sexual traumatization ($p < 0.05$) and poor sexual satisfaction in the partner relationship ($p < 0.05$).

Statistical tendencies indicated that earlier psychiatric difficulties, and in the six months before the assault, somatic health problems, a negative relation with the partner, and to have experienced violence between her own parents could be associated with depression one year post-assault.

A high degree of experienced social support served as a protective factor.

8.3.4.3. Factors Related to the Acute Response

One individual acute response variable was significantly related to long-term depression, namely a high degree of shame (CPRS score >3). Negative attitudes from others, such as being blamed by close network ($p < 0.05$) and a perceived negative reaction from the police ($p < 0.02$), were also significantly related to an outcome of depression.

To be understood and supported by friends and not being blamed by anyone served as protective factors as regards depression too.

8.3.4.4. A Predictive Index for Long-term Depressive Symptoms

The strongest combination of independent factors was: (1) violent or sexual traumatization in the past, (2) more than one offender and (3) a perceived negative reaction from the police. This index gives a sensitivity of 100 percent, a specificity of 67 percent and a positive predictive power of 48 percent.

8.3.5. CHARACTERISTICS OF THE WORST OUTCOME GROUP (N = 7)

Since this group got worse in the course of the first year (see Chapter 6) and since not all of them had the same diagnosis (see Chapter 7), it is of clinical interest to see which risk factors they shared. They had all been exposed to violent rapes, the violence/threat factor was shared by all and this was the most common factor. The majority (five) had no history of psychiatric symptoms in the past. More than half (four) experienced little social support and were blamed (five) by close network persons in the acute phase.

8.4. Discussion

Although there is an overlap between the different symptom groups, the predictors should give the clinician indications about who are the victims at risk, as well as which themes are important in the treatment of the individual patient.

Psychiatric functional impairment in the past, as well as earlier traumatization, play a role in the development of both PTSD as well as persistent depressive symptoms. However, with depression this is probably related to the fact that women who also had depressive symptoms before the rape were not excluded. Although no one was found to have had a PTSD in the time prior to the rape, depressive and anxiety symptoms were frequently reported in the group with psychiatric functional impairment in the past and earlier traumatization. The rape might in these cases merely have triggered a PTSD caused by a former trauma. The clinical consequence of this could be long-term treatment in which the former traumatization has to be dealt with too. However, these pre-rape variables were not enough for a PTSD development and half of those who developed PTSD did so without this background. Moderate post-traumatic stress symptoms were not linked to these background factors, which also indicates that it is the severity and combination of the symptoms that might be influenced by these factors. The main predictor for PTSD was the violence/threat factor, which was a condition for developing PTSD. Thus, in this study, PTSD is associated with a violent/threatening rape, whereas depressive symptoms seem to be more associated with factors related to violation of worth. If one compares this with the types of rape described in Chapter 4, "the violent rape" seems to be more linked to the development of PTSD, whereas the development of depression is more linked to the description of "the sexual rape". However, the fact that some victims who develop PTSD are very depressed and some not, could be explained by the different experience of degrading and humiliating aspects of the rape, and of variance with the victim's perception of her own performance during the ordeal. The lack of depressive symptoms in women who had not consumed any alcohol, who had been assaulted by a stranger and who had resisted actively points in this direction. These factors, however, do not seem to influence the long-term post-traumatic anxiety, the main feature of the post-traumatic stress symptoms.

The individual acute response to rape does not turn out to be a predictor of PTSD or of long-term depressive symptoms in this study. This is not in accordance with Kilpatrick's study in which initial distress was a predictor of long-term distress (Kilpatrick et al., 1985). Since the mean values on all acute reaction scores were higher in the PTSD outcome group, it is possible that the acute response might have shown a significant association in a larger sample.

The results as regards prediction of sexual disorders make it clear that the rape must have had a considerable impact of a certain kind. Depression, feelings of having been damaged and depersonalization are probably connected with disappointment and loss, a belief that she has been destroyed as a woman and that the only way to deal with this is by dissociating from her body. Statistical methods have not been able to identify one assault variable which explains this. The qualitative information we have on what the victims experienced as the worst aspect of being raped tells us that many of the women in this group had difficulties in verbalizing just that.

The results in this longitudinal study confirm Kilpatrick's retrospective study on crime-related PTSD, which concluded that the threat aspect is of importance for the development of PTSD. In this study the report of violent acts and/or threat or use of weapon was a better predictor than experienced death threat.

The only longitudinal studies which have focused on specific symptom groups are the studies on post-rape depression. Some of the present results – mental and somatic health problems before the rape and a negative reaction from network – are in accordance with the results in these studies.

Lastly, the search for predictors in this study is not a search for aetiology, but a search to identify victims at risk at an early stage. All the women in this study were given crisis intervention. For victims at risk this does not seem to be sufficient. A focus on coping with post-traumatic stress anxiety, issues of self-worth and shame and sexual issues should be taken into account in relation to the specific predictors of PTSD, depressive symptoms and sexual disorders.

The present results should be considered with caution. First, the appropriateness of applying logistic regression to such a small sample may be debated. Since the sample was small, three covariables at most were included in each logistic regression analysis. This should make the method appropriate. Secondly, as not all women at risk are identified in the analysis (see the results on sensitivity, specificity and positive predictive power), the risk factors cannot be treated as absolute. However, if the predictors are used as guidelines for the clinician in the effort to prevent long-term psychiatric problems they could be a valuable contribution. A factor not yet looked into in relation to outcome is the importance of coping strategy. This will be dealt with in the next chapter.

8.5. Conclusion

Factors identified in the acute phase turned out to have a predictive value not only for psychiatric outcome one year after rape but also for the development of specific disorders. The results could have clinical implications in the prevention of long-term disorders. Crisis intervention in the acute phase is not sufficient for victims at risk. Victims of completed rape with little social support have to receive extra attention. Further implications for treatment regarding the prevention of the specific disorders will be presented in Chapter 11.

The predictive indices do not pick out all victims at risk and the results should be handled with caution.

9

Change, Growth and Coping

9.1. Introduction

Psychological change in women who have been through a rape ordeal covers far more than reactions and symptoms. In order to understand the victim it is relevant to look at other dimensions besides psychiatric outcome and prediction. Changes in relation to self and others, coping efforts, as well as comparing those who managed well and those who did not, might give useful information to professionals who meet the victim in a therapeutic context.

The definition and measurement of coping are under discussion in stress research literature (Haan, 1982; Cohen, 1987). In relation to traumatic stress, Roth and Cohen identified two basic modes of coping with acute stress: approach and avoidance (Roth and Cohen, 1986). Their model is in accordance with Horowitz's model of response to traumatic stress and the process of "working through" (Horowitz, 1982). This model, which is of clinical relevance, has not so far been applied specifically in research regarding coping with rape. The aim of this chapter therefore is to answer the following questions:

(1) What changes do the women describe in relation to self and others apart from psychiatric reactions and symptoms, and how are these changes related to a psychiatric outcome?
(2) Will an avoidance/approach model for coping be useful when applied to psychiatric outcome?

9.2. Method

The data presented in this chapter on **changes in relation to self and others** are from the final assessment, when the women were asked about these changes. For example: "Do you think your self-confidence is the same as before?" If not, "Is it better than before or worse than before?" The term self-confidence was not operationalized, but simply reflects how the women understood the term. In addition, their answers were compared with their social network diagrams at two points in time, the first and the last assessment (see Chapter 3). A score on satisfaction in the partner relationship from the first and the last assessment (general and sexual) also formed the basis for the reported change in partner relationship (see Chapter 3). The self-statements on changes in relationships and the changes on these instruments were compared. All changes in partner relationships were confirmed by changes in satisfaction scores. However, the changes in the social network diagrams were more difficult to evaluate. Sometimes a statement like "I feel closer to my parents" was reflected in a different position of the parents in the diagram, but, especially if the parent was already placed among "significant, close others" in the first assessment, this change would not be apparent in the diagram. In these cases the subjective experience expressed in the self-statement formed the basis for the coding.

The data on **positive meaning and positive change** come from two open-ended questions in the final assessment, namely: "Sometimes when people have been through a painful experience they say that, although this was difficult and painful, it also led to something positive. Has the ordeal you have been through had any such positive meaning for you? Has the experience led to any positive change in your life?"

In the present study, any conscious effort to come to terms with what has happened and deal with the the post-rape reactions, symptoms and problems is defined as **coping**. No coping is labelled functional or dysfunctional, the point rather being to see whether the mode of coping is related to outcome.

The data on coping come from all three assessments; the women were simply asked to describe, at three different points in time, how they had dealt with the memory and their emotional reactions and symptoms after the rape. The coping strategies from all three assessments were written down as one coping description for every participant. The answers were coded into mainly avoidance-oriented, mixed or mainly approach-oriented coping strategies. Avoidance strategies were defined as conscious efforts to avoid the memory of the rape as well as the emotional consequences and post-assault problems. Approach was defined as a conscious effort to approach the memory of the rape as well as the emotional consequences and problems. Victims, their network and professionals who meet them at different stages so often ask the following questions: "Isn't it better to try to forget the whole thing, leave it alone and let time heal? Or is it better to face the pain and get it over with?" This was an opportunity to test the experience of a whole sample over time, tò find out what happens when one approaches painful memories and emotions and what happens if one avoids them, or balances between the two strategies.

Avoidance strategies could be cognitive – avoid thinking about it, push it aside, think about something else, tell myself to pretend it did not happen – or behavioural – keep myself in activity in order not to think/feel, distract myself by being with other people, listen to music etc. or drink alcohol to calm myself. Approach strategies could also be cognitive – think through what happened, try to understand – or behavioural – seek information about rape, talk about it to someone, practise doing the things one fears, working with self-defence, express emotions.

Example of mainly avoidance-oriented coping strategy:

> "I try to push it aside every time it comes back. I have tried not to think about it, never talk about it, I pretend, tell myself, it never happened. I know it happened, but I pretend it did not. I have done everything possible to forget it. I only told the doctor who examined me, you and my partner."

Example of a mixed avoidance-approach strategy:

> "I told my parents and my friends. There are periods when I really need to talk about it because it all comes back, then I talk to my friends. In these periods I also have tried to get some more information about rape and psychological reactions. Otherwise I have tried to live as normally as possible and not think about it, kept myself active in order not to think, tried to suppress it. When I panic, I give myself a good talking to. I have sometimes done things I was scared of to prove to myself that I could do them; that helped!"

Example of mainly approach-oriented strategy:

> "I talked to good friends about what happened, I went through it with you and especially with two friends and my husband. I forced myself to go to work, when my face looked normal again, even though I did not want to. But I knew I had to go through it sooner or later. I try to look the devil in the eye. After the first weeks I started to practise being alone, and all the other things that were difficult, but important in order to function. I told myself that I

would manage. There are things I still don't do, like walking alone in a deserted street late at night, but I have not considered it important; actually I think it is a rather foolish thing to do. I have done practical things, work that made me exhausted, so that afterwards I could tell myself: look, you have done something useful today."

The findings on changes in relation to self and others as well as on coping are related to the psychiatric outcome and no psychiatric outcome groups, which were presented in Chapter 7.

Reliability. In relation to coping, the written descriptions were categorized in the same manner independently by another psychiatrist experienced in psychotherapeutic work with traumatized patients. Cohen's kappa was used to measure reliability. The mean kappa was 0.69.

When comparing frequencies in two groups, a two-sided exact Fisher–Irwin test was used to see whether the differences were statistically significant.

9.3. Changes in Relation to Self and Others

9.3.1. CHANGES IN RELATION TO SELF

9.3.1.1. Self-confidence

The participant's statements about change in their self-confidence revealed that approximately half of them thought that their self-confidence was unchanged or had improved, whereas the rest felt it had worsened or found the question difficult to answer.

The significant difference between the psychiatric outcome group and the no psychiatric outcome group is described in Table 9.1.

Table 9.1 *Victims' reported change in self-confidence in the psychiatric outcome group (PO) and no psychiatric outcome group (no PO) one year post-assault*

Change in self-confidence	PO		No PO		p-value
	No.	%	No.	%	
More self-confidence	0	0	9	38	$p < 0.01$
Unchanged	6	26	8	33	n.s.
Less self-confidence	13	57	6	25	$p < 0.05$
Uncertain	4	17	1	4	n.s.
Total	23	100	24	100	

N = 47.

Table 9.2 *Victims' reported change in belief in own capacity to deal with difficulties in the psychiatric outcome group (PO) and no psychiatric outcome group (no PO) one year post-assault*

Belief in own capacity to deal with difficulties	PO No.	%	No PO No.	%
Stronger belief in own capacity	6	26	9	38
Unchanged	3	13	6	25
Less belief in own capacity	12	52	4	17
Uncertain/don't know	2	9	5	20
Total	23	100	24	100

N = 47.

9.3.1.2. Belief in Own Capacity to Deal with Difficulties

When asked about changed belief in their own capacity to cope with difficulties in general, the positive answers increased. The number of those who had increased belief in their own capacity to handle difficulties compared with those who now had less belief was approximately the same. The statistically significant difference between the psychiatric outcome and no psychiatric outcome group is in the area of decreased belief ($p < 0.05$).

As Table 9.2 demonstrates, the difference is mainly in the area of decreased belief.

9.3.1.3. Loss of Skills

Twenty-eight (60 percent) said at the final follow-up that there were things they could do before that they could not do anymore. This concerned a whole range of behaviour – from walking alone in the dark, travelling alone, concentrating, talking to people they did not know, or having an intimate relationship with a man.

9.3.1.4. New Skills

On the other hand, 23 (50 percent) said they had also acquired new skills, that there were things they could do now that they could not do before.

Examples of new skills

"I have learned to cope with anxiety."
"I have learned to endure difficulties."
"I have learned to be aware of danger."

"I am better at taking decisions, I trust my own judgement more."
"I represent myself better in confrontations with others."
"I am better at setting limits and do not let anybody exploit me."
"I am better at rejecting men I don't like in a decisive manner."

9.3.1.5. Positive Meaning and Positive Change

Twenty-six women (55%) gave a positive answer to the question about "any positive meaning" and 23 (50 percent) to the question about "any positive change". A positive answer to at least one of the questions was given by 7 of the 23 in the psychiatric outcome group (30 percent), whereas 21 of the 24 (87 percent) in the no psychiatric outcome group gave a positive answer, which is a significant difference ($p < 0.001$).

The answers about positive meaning or positive change fell into two categories: one category was related mainly to self, the other mainly concerned their relationship to others.

Examples of category one

"I have understood that I have a right to take care of myself – I don't let other people trample on me anymore."
"I have come to know myself better; I feel more confident knowing that I can handle very painful things, I feel stronger now."
"I have come to understand that even when something very negative happens, one must not give up. It has changed my view on what it is possible to deal with."
"I take my own life and my own responsibility for it much more seriously – life is no joke."
"What happened was so bad, it forced me to stop and think about my life and made me change it."

Examples of category two

"I am closer to my partner."
"I am closer to the people I want to be close to, and have more distance from people who are not important to me."
"I have much more compassion and understanding for people who have experienced sexual assault."

"I don't challenge fate by trusting people I don't know anymore; that change has been both positive and negative."
   "I take relationships with other people more seriously, am more conscious of who I confide in."
   "I recognize better a good relationship from one which is not worthwhile."

9.3.2. CHANGE IN RELATIONSHIPS WITH OTHERS

9.3.2.1. Family and Friends

As noted above, a change in close relations could be connected with a judgement of positive change. The victims were also asked to report changes in specific relationships. The women's own evaluation of change in relationships in the psychiatric outcome and no psychiatric outcome group are shown in Table 9.3. Better/closer relationship with family was more often reported in the no psychiatric outcome group, but the difference is not statistically significant. The significant difference ($p < 0.01$) was seen in worsened relations with friends; this was felt more by the psychiatric outcome group in comparison with the no psychiatric outcome group.

9.3.2.2. Relationship with Partner

At the time of the rape, 26 of the women had a relationship with a partner. Four of them were among the drop-outs and in three of

Table 9.3 *Evaluation of change in relationships with family and friends in the psychiatric outcome group (PO) and no psychiatric outcome group (no PO) one year post-assault*

Change in relationships	Family				Friends			
	PO		No PO		PO		No PO	
	No.	%	No.	%	No.	%	No.	%
Better/closer	6	26	10	42	1	4	6	24
Unchanged	8	35	12	50	10	43	12	50
Worse	6	26	1	4	11	48	3	13
Some better, some worse	0	0	1	4	0	0	3	13
Don't know	3	13	0	0	1	4	0	0
Total	23	100	24	100	23	99	24	100

N = 47.

these cases the partner was the offender. Nine had broken off the relationship with their partner, while 13 had the same partner in the last assessment as one year previously. The breaking up of relationships was interpreted by the participants as a consequence of the rape event in all cases except one, mainly because of post-rape sexual difficulties. The broken relationships tended to have been of shorter duration than the stable ones, except for one abusive relationship. Of the lasting relationships, two relationships were reported unchanged, seven better/closer and four worse.

Thirteen had established a relationship with a new partner at the time of the follow-up. Six of them judged the rape to have had a negative influence on the new relationship, three thought it had had no influence and four regarded it as having a positive influence. The negative influence was mainly on sexual relations and trust, the positive influence was related to the women's appreciation of a man who was supportive and understanding, including in the sexual area.

9.3.2.3. Change in Relation to Men in General

Five women reported no change in relation to men they did not know, the majority 29 (62 percent) reported that they were more on guard when they met men they did not know, and 13 (28 percent) said that they had avoided men they did not know during the last year. In relation to men they knew, 22 (47 percent) reported no change, whereas 19 (40 percent) were more on guard, 2 (4 percent) avoided men they knew and 4 (9 percent) felt safer with men they knew after the rape.

9.4. Coping

From the women's descriptions at the three assessments of what they did/had done to handle their own reactions and deal with what had happened, it was apparent that most victims had used a wide variety of cognitive and behavioural strategies. The coding of the coping strategies into mainly avoidance, mainly approach-oriented or mixed revealed that the avoidance or alternately avoidance/ approach-oriented strategies were most usual, but also that there were differences in the mode of coping in the different outcome

Table 9.4 *Main mode of coping in the psychiatric outcome group (PO) and no psychiatric outcome group (no
PO) one year post-assault*

Main mode of coping	PO No.	%	No PO No.	%
Mainly avoidance	15	65	3	13
Mixed	7	32	12	50
Mainly approach-oriented	1	2	9	37
Total	23	99	24	100

N = 47.

groups (see Table 9.4). The significant difference ($p < 0.01$) is in the dominant use of mainly avoidance strategies by the psychiatric outcome group compared with the no psychiatric outcome group.

Looking specifically at the worst outcome group (see Chapter 6), the avoidance coping strategy was a main characteristic for all of them.

Coping on a symbolic level. Eleven women (23 percent) reported that they had been actively working with themes that in content were to some extent related to the theme of rape, although they concerned other areas in life than sexual assault. They all felt this had been important in the recovery process. This could, for example, mean practising strategies/measures aimed against invasion from others, at being in control of one's own life or against bullying and domination from others.

"Every time I manage to set limits when I feel others exploit me, it has helped me somehow. I have become so conscious of it after the rape, as if the rape was an extreme of the same thing."
"It has become important to state my own opinion, not let others tell me what I should think/feel or how I think/feel."
"I seem to have made an issue of being treated respectfully at work [waitress]. Before I smiled politely when a customer pinched my behind, although I did not like it. Now, I don't accept it, nobody must ever treat me like that again."
"I do whatever possible to feel I am in control of the situation I am in; I think twice and take care of myself."

9.5. Discussion

The present study confirms that women frequently report changes in relation to self and significant others one year after rape. The negative changes are, not surprisingly, most prominent in the psychiatric outcome group. In relation to self, this is reflected in their assessment of self-confidence; in relation to others, it is reflected in the worsening of relationships with friends. Some women in the psychiatric outcome group also reported increased belief in their own capacity to handle difficulties. This reflects the fact that these women, in spite of their difficulties, had improved considerably in the course of the first year and made quite an effort to cope.

The no psychiatric outcome group reported few changes in relations with friends, but both groups showed that relationships with family could improve, although this was more frequent in the no psychiatric outcome group. This could mean that after rape, when women are frequently afraid to be alone, many seek refuge in their families, often resulting in more closeness, or disappointment and distance.

Whether the women in the psychiatric outcome group had closer friendships and therefore managed better is difficult to judge. The analysis of predictors (Chapter 8) shows that describing friends as the best helpers in the acute phase was related to a good outcome. This could mean that their friendships were of a better quality or that these women more easily sought and accepted support from friends.

Half of the steady relationships with men broke up in the course of the first year. These relationships were of shorter duration than the relationships that lasted, which could mean that they might have broken up anyway. However, the women usually attributed the breaking up to the rape, because of sexual difficulties afterwards. The change in relations with partners suggests that, although negative effects are apparent, they are probably also related to the quality of the relationship beforehand.

The results from the present study only partly confirm the finding from the the Charleston study of negative effects on relations with others, particularly parents (Murphy et al., 1988). The present study shows great variations within the whole sample, related mainly to outcome, and clearly indicates that relationships with friends might be more vulnerable than relationships with parents. But the studies are difficult to compare; the Charleston study was focused on a comparison between victims and non-victims, whereas the present study looks at differences within the victim group. The methodology is also different and the drop-out ratio is high in the other study. However, both studies demonstrate that a rape event has an impact, on both relations with self and relationships with others.

In Nadelson and Notman's study, signs of maturation and growth in the wake of a traumatic experience were described (Nadelson et al., 1982). This is in accordance with the present findings. These questions are rarely raised and should not be interpreted in the direction that rape can be a positive thing. In Norway, positive effects of the Second World War, such as social cohesion, are often mentioned. No one would, however, call the war a positive event. It is nevertheless of interest that even a very negative event does not exclude the possibility of personal growth and change. It also demonstrates the resources people can exhibit in times of suffering.

That such phenomena appeared significantly more in the no psychiatric outcome group could mean that this group was more able to find a meaning in the wake of a negative event and therefore showed more improvement. However, it could also mean that a more positive development and fewer after-effects make it easier for the person in question to identify such positive outcomes. The Nadelson and Notman study does not relate these changes to outcome.

The results on coping are difficult to compare with other studies on coping with rape since different categories have been used. Many of the adaptive strategies from Burgess and Holmstrom's study (1979) could be labelled avoidant – the maladaptive strategies mentioned are clearly avoidant. The difference in how outcome is evaluated also makes a comparison difficult. Roth and Cohen's approach/avoidance categorizations for coping with stress were selected because of their clinical relevance. The present results are tentative. However, the main differences between the psychiatric outcome and no psychiatric outcome groups point in the direction that the approach/avoidance categories are useful and that mode of coping may be of prime importance in the recovery from rape. Most of the data presented in this chapter represent the women's own statements of experienced change. The women's subjective evaluation of change and the differences between the psychiatric outcome and no psychiatric outcome group in this evaluation were the main interest.

The changes in relation to self and others showed interesting differences in the two outcome groups. In order to be confirmed by other studies the outcome measures should be comparable.

9.6. Conclusion

The present results confirm that changes in the victim's relation to self and others are frequent consequences of rape. The changes can be both negative and positive. Negative changes are associated with long-term psychiatric disorders after rape.

There is also a significant difference between the psychiatric outcome and no psychiatric outcome group concerning the coping strategies applied by the victims. Mainly avoidance strategies are associated with a psychiatric outcome, whereas an alternation of approach and avoidance strategies or mainly approach strategies are related to recovery. This result has clinical implications and confirms that to avoid talking about the traumatic event, to try to forget or pretend it never happened, should not be supported in the counselling of victims and their network.

10

Bodily Complaints and Somatic Health

10.1. Introduction

The main focus in this study has been the impact of rape on mental health. Other longitudinal studies have also focused mainly on the psychosocial consequences. However, people who suffer do not usually divide their psyche and soma in the way medical professionals do. Therefore the present investigation also included questions on somatic complaints.

The relationship between life stress and illness has been investigated in relation to gynaecological symptoms in several studies. Pelvic pain has been reported to be associated with recent experiences of life stress (Beard et al., 1988). Schei's study on physical and sexual abuse by spouse as a risk factor in gynaecological disorders shows that pelvic pain is strongly associated with living in a physically abusive relationship. She also shows a correlation between adverse sexual experiences, sexual abuse and pelvic pain. Exposure to an abusive relationship was also associated with pelvic inflammatory disease (Schei, 1990). Depression and the presence of threatening life-events are in combination and independently shown to be associated with a reduction of immune function (Bartrop et al., 1977; Irwin et al., 1990).

The present study did not measure biological changes such as stress hormones or indicators of the immune system. However, reported changes in health in general was a major concern. This chapter therefore will address the following questions:

(1) What were the immediate somatic health consequences of exposure to rape?
(2) Are there any changes in the women's reported somatic health problems pre- and post-assault? If so, are the changes in somatic health related to psychiatric disorders?
(3) What is the nature of the somatic health complaints post-assault?

10.2. Method

The data on changes in somatic health, changes in the use of somatic health services, bodily reactions and somatic complaints after rape stem from the first and the last assessment (see Chapter 3). At both assessments the participants were asked whether their somatic health had been as usual, better than usual or worse than usual during the previous year. They were also asked how many times they had consulted a physician for somatic complaints in the previous year. The specific nature of the somatic complaint was then investigated, written down and categorized. The categories were: complaints connected with the respiratory tract system, with the the cardio-vascular system, with the muscular–skeletal system, with the urinary system, with the gastro-intestinal system, with the endocrinological system and with gynaecological disturbance. The answers allowed for a comparison between the two reports on several answers. For instance, if a participant reported her health to have been as usual the previous year at the first assessment and worse at the last assessment, the report could be validated by the reports on the number of consultations in the previous year and the nature of the complaint. The self-rating scale for psychophysiological stress symptoms (SSL) gave some additional information. The information on immediate somatic consequences comes from the Emergency Ward records. The term "pelvic pain" is used in relation to pain in the pelvis not related to the menstrual cycle, and not related to intercourse. The findings on changes in somatic health are related to the psychiatric outcome group and no psychiatric outcome group presented in Chapter 7.

10.3. Immediate Somatic Consequences of the Rape

Three had become infected with venereal disease. One got pregnant, and chose to have an abortion. Post-operatively she got an infection, endometritis. Other injuries were mostly minor: two had fractured ribs, two had concussion due to heavy blows on their heads, one had a bite wound in her breast and one a knife wound in her thigh. About 45 percent has superficial excoriations or contusions.

The most prominent somatic reactions in the acute phase were the psychophysiological stress reactions already described in Chapter 5.

10.4. Changes in Reported Somatic Health in the Course of the First Year – Nature of Complaints

10.4.1. SELF-REPORTED CHANGES IN SOMATIC HEALTH AND RELATION TO PSYCHIATRIC OUTCOME

Twenty-one (45 percent) reported that their somatic health had been worse than in the year before the rape, and this was confirmed by their report from the first assessment. Eighteen of them reported an increase in their use of the somatic health service, both general practitioners and somatic specialists. Fifteen had been admitted to a somatic ward in the course of the first year after the rape, compared with three the year before. Most of the victims who reported worse health had more than one problem.

The frequency of somatic health complaints in the psychiatric outcome group compared with the no psychiatric outcome group is described in Table 10.1. The results demonstrate the statistically significant difference between the two groups, with little change in the no psychiatric outcome group and a reported worsening in the psychiatric outcome group. Reports on health during the year before the assault in the first assessment show no difference between the two groups. In the following, the nature of the complaints in the worse health group (N = 21, see Table 10.1) will be described. The two outcome groups will not be compared any further, as the numbers become too small.

10.4.2. INCREASE IN INFECTIONS

Sixteen in the worse health group reported that they had been bothered by repeated infections in the upper respiratory tract such

Table 10.1 *Changes in somatic health in the psychiatric outcome group (PO) and no psychiatric outcome group (no PO) one year post-assault.*

| Changes in somatic health | PO | | No PO | | |
	No.	%	No.	%	p-value
Better	0	0	1	4	n.s.
Unchanged	8	35	17	70	$p < 0.05$
Worse	15	65	6	26	$p < 0.01$
Total	23	100	24	100	

N = 47.

as colds, flu, bronchitis, sinusitis, to an extent that was unusual for them. Urinary and gynaecological infections and infections that were complications after surgical interventions were also reported as causes of worse health, but less frequently.

10.4.3. GASTRO-INTESTINAL COMPLAINTS

Nausea and/or stomach-ache/cramps were another problem in the worse health group; 16 reported that this had been a considerable problem in the course of the first year. Three had been admitted to hospital for acute abdominal pain and two were operated on because of suspected appendicitis, the third with suspected ileus. The first two were diagnosed as having lymphadenitis, the third had an ileus caused by adherent tissues.

10.4.4. PAINS CAUSED BY MUSCULAR TENSION

Pains such as headache, backache, aching shoulders, arms, etc. due to increased muscular tension were reported as a new complaint by eight women.

10.4.5. GYNAECOLOGICAL COMPLAINTS

Of the 15 women who had been admitted to hospital during the first year, 9 were admitted to gynaecological wards. Of these, two had salpingitis, two were spontaneous abortions, two were induced abortions (one of them got pregnant by the rapist), one was operated on for an extra-uterine pregnancy, one who had had endometriosis for years got an exacerbation with irregular bleeding, hæmaturia and pains and was hospitalized for abrasio and evaluation. The ninth was a planned hospitalization for an examination of infertility. Six women reported pelvic pain as a new complaint.

Changes in menstruation were also reported. Eight women developed amenorrhoea after the rape (not due to pregnancy), mostly in the course of the first few months and of 2–3 months' duration. One amenorrhoea was artificial – the woman who had been menstruating during the rape had developed a phobia for her own menstrual blood and took contraceptive pills continuously for six months to avoid her own bleeding. Eleven women (23 percent) reported irregular bleeding in contrast with the year before the rape. Increased dysmenorrhoea was reported by seven (15 percent) and stronger bleeding was reported by five (10 percent).

10.4.6. WORSENED CONDITION OF CHRONIC DISEASES

As already mentioned, exacerbation of chronic diseases was also reported in the first year after the rape. This was the case for four women: one had endometriosis, two had asthma and one had juvenile diabetes. The asthma patients had more and worse attacks than the previous year and were hospitalized several times – one of them twice, the other one four times, the last time for three weeks in a special lung clinic. The worsened condition for the patient with juvenile diabetes was self-inflicted; she became reckless about her diet and her injections.

10.5. Discussion

The report on somatic health shows that there is an increase in somatic health complaints in 45 percent of the sample in the first year after rape. The increase is greater in the psychiatric disorder group. Common complaints were an increase in infections, gastro-intestinal complaints, pains due to muscular tension, gynaecological complaints and worsening of chronic diseases.

Since none of the longitudinal studies using comparison groups has focused on somatic health, the findings in the present study should be confirmed. The presented findings should be regarded as exploratory. In Schei's study, a correlation was found between adverse sexual experiences, sexual abuse and pelvic pain. This combination was also associated with reported psychological problems (Schei, 1990). The increase in infections could point in the same direction as Irwin's study on the reduction of immune functions in life stress and depression (Irwin et al., 1990). If a future study on changes in somatic health after rape were conducted, it should include measures of stress hormones and of immune functions. Muscular pain and gastro-intestinal complaints are well-known psychophysiological stress symptoms and probably reflect the general state of increased arousal as part of the post-traumatic stress symptoms.

The data on changes in somatic health are mainly based on the self-report of the women. The validity of self-reported health data is discussed. The participants may tend to recall adverse events more easily after a rape than they did for the year before. In order to confirm the present results, a future study focusing on somatic health complaints could use a matching comparison group of non-raped women, as well as giving more consideration to methodology, such as evaluation and measurement procedures.

10.6. Conclusion

The present study of changes in somatic health after rape must be regarded as exploratory and the results should be confirmed by studies putting more emphasis on the evaluation of changes in somatic health. However, the results demonstrate the close connection between psychological and somatic distress. They also remind us of the important role of the general practitioner who is consulted by women suffering from rape-related complaints. The attentive physician has the opportunity also to detect psychiatric complaints and to evaluate whether the patient needs psychotherapeutic intervention.

11

General Discussion

In order to explore the after-effects of rape in relation to health, a longitudinal study of victims of rape was conducted. Rape was explored as "an event outside the range of normal human experience that would be markedly distressing to almost anyone". The post-traumatic stress nature of the reactions, symptoms and disorders following rape was specifically looked into. Risk factors from the acute phase which predicted long-term psychiatric outcome were identified. Coping strategies were explored and seen in relation to psychiatric outcome, as were changes in relation to self and others. Accompanying somatic health complaints have also been described. The results have partly been discussed in the chapters where they are presented. In this chapter I shall discuss some principal methodological and result issues more comprehensively.

11.1. The Research Questions Raised in the Present Study

The research questions in this study concern clinical rather than theoretical issues. The basic assumption behind the research questions is that the identification of problems, the understanding and knowledge about the nature of problems and the identification of factors that might influence outcome are useful to practitioners of medicine and psychology in order to understand and treat patients. However, a more specific assumption in the present study is that rape and its consequences for health should be investigated within the frame of a traumatic experience. Thus the post-traumatic stress nature of the reaction becomes a main issue in the investigation. Questions considering somatic health were included, although not extensively. They were included, however, because it is usually the general practitioners who are contacted initially, and the somatic complaints are often presented first. The link between the somatic and psychiatric complaints after rape is accordingly useful and relevant. Thus accompanying somatic health complaints were recorded and described.

The question of personality traits as a risk factor was left out. First, I consider personality tests to be inadvisable in the acute phase. Victims of rape are extremely vulnerable to questions about their personality, as they expect to be blamed. They are also often met with a blaming attitude. Personality inventories may easily be perceived as confirming such expectations. It is crucial not to do any harm in this situation. Secondly, in the acute phase when a person is dominated by emotional imbalance, I considered a personality evaluation to be less valid. Thirdly, I chose to select information that would be relatively easy to extract in the acute phase, also by emergency health workers not trained in personality evaluation.

The objective of the present study, to look at the consequences of rape in relation to the victim's health, can be questioned in itself. Metzger writes that the consequences of rape should be seen not as an illness to be cured, but as a loss to be mourned (Metzger, 1976). Esper has claimed that the reaction to rape is a normal and functional adaptive reaction to the discovery of a disturbing reality and is not psychopathology (Esper, 1986). I agree with the view-point that suffering should not automatically be diagnosed as illness and that there is a danger in medicalizing normal reactions to abnormal events. Where these reactions persist over time, how-ever, they may become dysfunctional and express themselves in ways that the medical profession will define as illness. The reality in the health service is that many women who suffer from disturbing distress as a consequence of a rape experience seek professional help. Their problems are often not identified and understood; as a consequence they receive inadequate treatment.

Thus, to make use of a diagnostic system appeared relevant. Because of its clear description of Post-Traumatic Stress Disorder (PTSD), the *Diagnostic and Statistical Manual of Mental Disorders* (third edition, revised, DSM-III-R) was chosen. Aware of the limitation of descriptive diagnosis in enhancing psychological understanding, I have explored the stressor through a qualitative analysis, presented case histories, used the women's own state-ments as examples and described the changes in relation to self and others.

11.2. Methodology

11.2.1. THE DESIGN

It is inherent in the design of a longitudinal study that it should be possible to record the traumatic experience and the immediate reaction at an early stage. The assault, the acute response as well as background factors can be recorded before the long-term consequences are known, and thus provide for unbiased identification of predictors of long-term mental health problems. To establish contact in the acute phase should also increase the likelihood of a satisfactory participation rate.

It could be argued that a longer follow-up than one year might yield better information concerning long-term consequences. However, earlier projects have shown that rape victims are difficult to follow up (Binder, 1981; Kilpatrick, 1985). A one-year follow-up is more realistic and is sufficient to give a clear picture of the course of the reaction and the nature of post-rape problems as a source for the analysis of predictors. It is also easier to evaluate the link with the traumatic experience within such a time-span.

A comparison group design was decided against, as the aim of the study was not to find out whether rape victims develop mental health problems compared with a group that have not been raped. Such studies have already been performed (Ellis, 1983). In the present study it was assumed that comparison within the victim group would be of more interest from a clinical perspective.

11.2.2. THE SAMPLE AND ITS REPRESENTATIVENESS

The present sample was a selection of women seeking emergency help in Oslo during a ten-month period. Information about the service had been widely publicized and it was the only service available (see Chapter 1). The women who attended the Emergency Ward should therefore be representative of rape victims who seek emergency help in the acute phase in Oslo. According to the official reports from the Ward, the women in the present sample should be representative according to sociodemographic variables and assault characteristics (Bang, 1986, 1988).

Compared with the longitudinal studies from USA, where the sample sources have mostly been hospital-based rape crisis centres, the present sample does not differ essentially in the age or marital status of the victims (Burgess and Holmstrom, 1974; Calhoun et al., 1982; Kilpatrick et al., 1981). Whether the women in the present study are representative of rape victims in general is unknown. Random population surveys indicate that many rape victims do not report the crime or seek help and that rape in close relationships is less likely to be reported and is more frequent than other rapes

(Russel, 1985; Schei, 1990). However, the present sample should be representative of victims seeking emergency help and thus of major interest for the health service and for preventive psychiatry. When looking more closely at the sample it seems to differ slightly from a normal population of women of that age group. Relatively many (26.4 percent) have had psychiatric problems with fuctional impairment in the past, and in 64 percent the psychiatric problems were combined with substance-abuse problems. In an epidemiological study in Oslo in 1991, 19.4 percent of the female population had a psychiatric morbidity measured on HSCL (Hopkins Symptom Checklist), which primarily measures anxiety and depressive symptoms (Sandanger et al., 1992). Psychiatric morbidity is higher in the sample group and probably also indicates more serious conditions since functional impairment is emphasized. I have supervised the staff at the Emergency Ward in relation to their work with the admission of rape victims for six years and, although this has not been documented in any reports, it is my clear impression that the present sample does not essentially differ regarding pre-assault psychiatric problems. Women are vulnerable to assault if they are in a vulnerable situation, whether because they are weak or unprotected for behavioural reasons, they lack self-respect or they are alone in a deserted area accidentally.

Of the women with earlier psychiatric impairment, 78 percent had also experienced sexual or violent traumatization before the age of 16, which might also be a vulnerability factor.

Of those invited to participate in the present study, 24 percent declined. They did not differ significantly on sociodemographic variables, but the figures indicate that more of them might have been in a socially difficult situation (substance abusers, unemployed). This group could have been either less distressed or more ashamed and avoidant. Some may have given false reports. The offer of contact with a psychiatrist may also have influenced the sampling towards a more distressed group. However, referrals to psychiatric outpatient units or family guidance clinics were presented as alternatives. Some of the participants also stressed that they did not want treatment, but would participate in the study if it could be helpful to others. A participation rate of 76 percent is considerably higher than in other studies where in-depth interviews and standardized measurements have been performed, and in rape research this figure must be considered satisfactory.

The sample also consisted of two men who have been excluded from this work. These men were, however, followed up in the same manner as the women. The difficulty of investigating the psychological impact of homosexual rapes is linked to the difficulty of getting a sufficient sample size.

11.2.3. THE ASSESSMENTS

A combination of standardized measurements and semi-structured interviews was chosen as the assessment method in the present study. A choice of solely standardized or qualitative methods was decided against. Standardized methods alone would give inadequate information concerning the individual experience and the personal meaning of the assault. Standardization is concerned with how to ask all respondents the same questions and how to analyze their responses within standardized coding systems. This line of inquiry will not open the way to new information about phenomena, and it neglects the problems of context and meaning and an understanding of how interviews work (Mishler, 1986). Standardization, however, provides the opportunity to use indicators of health, to compare reactions over time, and to compare indicators of health within the participant group and with other studies.

An important question is whether the choice of instruments could have been different and eventually lead to different results. Instruments that do not include post-traumatic stress items would certainly have missed the identification of post-traumatic stress symptoms. The results would then probably have emphasized anxiety and phobic symptoms, as the other longitudinal studies have demonstrated (Ellis, 1983). DSM-III (1980) and DSM-III-R (1987) categorize PTSD as an anxiety disorder. Also in the present study the consequence of post-traumatic trauma-avoidance is phobic behaviour, and involuntary re-experiences (intrusion) are significantly related to anxiety level (Chapters 5 and 7).

The choice of measurements was directed by the fact that they had proved useful in other logintudinal studies of traumatized populations; they were short and they made sense to a person in the acute stage of victimization. The extended version of the Comprehensive Psychopathological Rating Scale (CPRS), CPRS-PTSD, was preferred to measure psychopathological symptoms since it demonstrates changes over time when one compares scores from two points in time, e.g. acute phase versus one year later. It is also useful for diagnostic purposes because it clearly indicates when a symptom reaches a level of dysfunction. In the last assessment, when a diagnostic procedure was required, the Structural Clinical Interview for DSM-III (SCID) as a reliable instrument for diagnosis would also have been highly relevant. However, to use the full SCID in addition to the extended CPRS, an interview that in itself is time-consuming and tiring, was completely unrealistic. It would also have entailed asking about the same complaints twice. The solution found was to use SCID for additional information not covered by the CPRS–PTSD and as a helpful guide in the diagnostic procedure.

A qualitative method, including a qualitative analysis, in the investigation of the nature of the stressor was considered highly relevant, as the nature of the trauma itself has not been explored in relation to research.

11.2.4. VALIDITY AND RELIABILITY

In psychiatric and psychological research, questions of validity in relation to quantitative methods are concerned with the relationship between a measuring instrument and what it attempts to measure, while reliability concerns the accuracy or consistency of a measuring procedure (Lewin, 1979; Friis and Vaglum, 1986). In qualitative research, the term validity refers to whether what one has found is well grounded and supportable (Polkinghorne, 1988). Here verification is not a final product cont.ol; validation is built into the research process, with continual checks on the credibility, plausibility and trustworthiness of the actual strategies for collecting, coding, analysing and presenting the data (Glaser and Strauss, 1967). Reliability in narrative study usually refers to the dependability of the data, and validity to the strength of the analysis of the data (Polkinghorne, 1988).

The majority of the standardized measures used in the present study have been used in other studies with traumatized populations and have been proved valid and reliable. In addition, the reliability of the CPRS–PTSD scores was tested with Cohen's kappa, with a mean kappa of 0.73 (see Chapter 7). This result should be considered satisfactory.

The statistically significant difference between the group diagnozed as having psychiatric disorder and the non-diagnostic group on all measures supported the identification of the diagnostic group (see Chapter 7). The diagnostic procedure would probably have been considered even more reliable if another psychiatrist had repeated them. However, in order to do that, the other person would have had to go through not only the last assessment, but also the initial assessment, which would have been extremely demanding for someone not involved. Instead, the question of the diagnosis, particularly when the evaluation was difficult, was discussed with the main supervisor of the project, Professor Lars Weisæth, by oral presentation of the cases.

The categorization of coping strategies into mainly avoidance, mixed or approach-oriented was scored independently by another psychiatrist from written descriptions, and here the mean kappa was 0.69 (see Chapter 9). These results should be regarded as fairly good, since the categorization of coping strategies represented interpretations of descriptive qualitative data.

The data collection for the qualitative analysis as well as the details of the analysis itself have been described so that the reader can make his/her own judgement of whether the results are well grounded. Qualitative analysis is by nature interpretive and the ideal of scholarly consensus is preferred to tests of mathematical validity (Polkinghorne, 1988). The analysis is based on questions asked to each narrative. The questions arise from how the event is understood by the researcher; not as an impact agent, but as an interpersonal experience told by the injured party. If this assumption is found acceptable, the reader will be able to evaluate the analytical questions and the description of the different patterns. The description of the event by a traditional frequency recording of different variables supports the main features of the interpreted descriptions.

The collection of data in this study was done in a clinical context. The participants were seeking help and within that context they received the invitation to participate and were assessed. This should also be taken into account when the validity of the information is considered. The participants volunteered to attend the study after they had been through a thorough admission at the Emergency Ward and often they had also been thoroughly interrogated by the police. It is not likely that anyone who had not been exposed to an assault would have chosen to come to a psychiatrist for a detailed interview after these initial procedures, and it is not likely that a detailed interview about the event as described in Chapter 4 could have been carried out without uncovering a false report. There was a certain tendency, though, to withhold particularly distressing or shame-related information, or to make an initial denial of being distressed. Usually this was revealed during the interview sessions after the initial contact. The problems with the trustworthiness of the information therefore seemed to be related more to denial and avoidance than to exaggeration.

Information from other sources than the participants themselves, such as the emergency admission, the health insurers, primary care physicians and family members, represented mainly an opportunity to check information about those where the information was available. No essential contradictions came out of this information.

11.3. A Brief Discussion of the Main Results

11.3.1. THE STRESSOR – AN EVENT OUTSIDE THE RANGE OF NORMAL HUMAN EXPERIENCES?

Do the results in the present study confirm that rape *per se* is an event outside the range of normal human experiences as defined in criterion A of PTSD in DSM-III-R? Or is rape a trivial matter and its impact exaggerated? Or can it be both, depending on the circumstances?

No participant in the present study was unaffected by the event in the acute phase; the event was distressing to everyone. Moderate to severe post-traumatic stress symptoms were present in all cases (see Chapter 5). Experienced life-threat during rape was present in the majority of cases (79 percent), but not all. In the completed rape cases, forcible penetration represents a threat to physical integrity whether the use of violence is minimal or considerable. The emotional reaction to the penetration (numbing and/or dissociation) was astonishingly similar and underlines that this factor is of special importance in the trauma of rape. However, the definition of the A criterion and the term "threat to physical integrity" can be interpreted differently. Weisæth claims that, to meet the A criterion, the event must be extreme and *life-threatening* (Weisæth, 1991). Rape is always a threat to physical integrity, but is not always experienced as a threat to life. For example, the person who is attacked while sleeping might experience only a brief sensation of danger. A different threat is involved: the annihilation of the person as a psychological and sexual being. The assault on physical integrity is linked to that.

For the development of long-term PTSD, however, a violence/threat factor was a condition. This supports Weisæth's emphasis on the danger aspect. Weisæth's own study on an industrial disaster found that the risk of long-term PTSD was associated with exposure to danger (Weisæth, 1984). But traumas of violence involving human interaction are more complex. Even if extreme threat or danger is a condition for the development of long-term PTSD, it does not follow that "an event that is outside the range of human experience and that would be markedly distressing to almost anyone" has to be limited to a situation of extreme physical danger. The view that the A criterion for PTSD should be limited to such events should not be adopted before the traumatic elements of several different traumas of violence involving direct human interaction, such as torture and abuse, have been more thoroughly explored.

11.3.2. THE MENTAL HEALTH PROBLEMS POST-ASSAULT

To use indicators of health such as diagnosis to identify health problems after rape will not give the same results as a recording of everyone with reactions/symptoms. The women's own evaluation of recovery is also different; a greater number do not consider themselves as recovered. A clinical diagnostic procedure will generally select the subjects who are more troubled by their symptoms and experience greater functional impairment. The results in the present study also indicate that they are far more troubled by somatic complaints. Thus the diagnostic procedure is used as an instrument to select the group that is most likely to be in need of the health service. Earlier longitudinal studies have focused on recovery or have investigated different symptoms (Burgess and Holmstrom, 1974; Nadelson et al., 1982; Atkeson et al., 1982; Kilpatrick, 1985), without focusing on who will be most likely to need therapeutic assistance.

The results show an overlap between the different disorders and emphasize the post-traumatic stress nature of e.g. sexual disorders in this study. Depression, however, could represent another type of reaction to the trauma of rape. The diagnostic procedure might also serve as an instrument for the selection of treatment. Even though coping with the memory of the traumatic experience and its consequences might be the core of the treatment, post-assault depression, say, will require different treatment from a PTSD or a sexual disorder. When appearing together this will still be the case. For preventive intervention and early treatment the predictive factors could give useful guidance.

11.3.3. THE PREDICTIVE FACTORS

The results on predictive factors have to take into consideration the fact that the sample is small, with the weaknesses this represents for statistical analysis. It is therefore necessary to present what supports the result, both in the present study and in other studies.

11.3.3.1. The Predictive Index for the Whole Diagnostic Group

The predictive index turned out to be penetration and lack of social support. That penetration was a condition for the development of any long-term problems after rape in the present study can of course be disputed by the fact that there were few attempted rapes. A comparison of the psychiatric after-effects in an equal number of attempted and completed rapes might have given an opportunity to test out the importance of penetration as a predictive factor more thoroughly.

That penetration represented a condition for any psychiatric after-effect is in any case a strong indicator that should be investigated further. The emotional impact of the penetration during rape provides further evidence that this factor is important.

Low social support as a predictive factor was confirmed by other related factors, namely blame from close network and a negative relation to partner. The importance of social support after a stressful event has also been found in other studies (Cobb, 1976; Solomon, 1986; Holen, 1990).

11.3.3.2. The Predictive Index for PTSD

Here a violence/threat factor was highly significant and a condition for a PTSD outcome. The importance of this factor has been pointed out before in relation to both rape and disaster (Weisæth, 1984; Kilpatrick et al., 1989).

The second factor was earlier functional impairment owing to psychiatric symptoms, which was also highly significant. To have received psychiatric treatment was also related to a PTSD outcome. However, this factor had to be combined with the violence/threat factor to have an effect. Half of the PTSD outcome group did not come into this category, demonstrating that rape as a stressor can result in a PTSD outcome even if the person does not have this vulnerability factor.

The same was found by Weisæth (1984); psychiatric impairment in the past turned out to be a vulnerability factor when it was combined with high-stress exposure, but the stressor itself could also precipitate PTSD.

The third factor was blame, which was an important additional factor when there was no prior psychiatric history and was also highly significant. The importance of this factor was supported by an association with a PTSD outcome and low social support and a positive relation between no PTSD and a high level of experienced social support. The acute response was not significantly related to long-term PTSD, as for example in Weisæth's study (1984). All the acute response measures were higher in the PTSD outcome group, but the difference did not reach statistical significance. It is thus possible that a larger sample would come up with acute response variables as predictive factors too.

11.3.3.3. The Predictive Index for Sexual Disorders

This index consists of two factors. The first indicates that satisfaction with life before the rape makes the person more susceptible to the development of sexual disorders after rape. This factor is supported by the tendencies of other data, namely good health, no visits to the doctor the year before the rape, no earlier somatic or psychiatric problems and low age.

The other predictive factor was a high depression score in the acute phase. Other acute response variables were also associated with a sexual disorder outcome, such as depersonalization and a feeling of being damaged. This means that a young, healthy person, whose acute reaction after rape is dominated by depression, depersonalization and a feeling of having been damaged, seems to be more at risk of developing a sexual disorder. Since the results cannot be compared with other studies, the results must be seen as tentative and should be confirmed by further studies.

11.3.3.4. The Predictive Index for Depression

The predictors of depression were former traumatization, more than one offender and a negative reaction from the police.

That former traumatization serves as a predictive factor could be related to the inclusion of women with earlier depressive problems. The assault and acute response factors become more interesting when they are seen in relation to the other associated factors and the statistical tendencies of association. These were intense shame reaction in the acute phase, intake of alcohol, a social prelude to the rape, a variety of sexual acts, obeying orders from the offender and negative reactions from others in the acute phase. In contrast, factors related to non-depression were to be assaulted by a stranger, not to have consumed alcohol, to have resisted actively and to have received a high degree of social support. This information supports a hypothesis that depression after a rape experience is related to humiliation, shame and issues concerning self-esteem.

A larger sample would have made it possible to exclude the formerly depressed and might have come up with other results. However, the results at hand might still be of clinical relevance.

11.3.4. COPING

The role of coping strategy in the recovery from rape revealed a statistically significant difference between the psychiatric outcome group compared with the no psychiatric outcome group. The results indicating that use of a mainly avoidant coping strategy does not pay are supported by the sole use of this strategy in the worst outcome group. It is possible that Weisæth's emphasis on "lack of motivation to fight the anxiety" or "lack of a contraphobic attitude" as a factor that influenced outcome in his study refers to the same phenomenon (Weisæth, 1984).

11.4. Suggestions for Further Research

The present study suggests some new questions:

(1) What is the traumatic impact of the forced penetration in itself? This matter can be explored further in two directions. One is to investigate the impact of forced penetration on women specifically through qualitative investigations contrasting forced penetration with women's experience of normal sexual intercourse. The other is to compare an equal number of victims of attempted and completed rape and investigate penetration as a risk factor for long-term psychiatric outcome. It would also be of interest to study the effects of forced penetration on men and compare the traumatic impact on men and women. The difficulty in conducting such a study is linked to the difficulty of getting a sufficient number of participants.

(2) Will the predictive factors for sexual disorders and depression be confirmed by other studies? This question could be investigated within the frame of the above-mentioned study comparing attempted and completed rapes.
(3) Is there a connection between biological indicators of stress and somatic reactions after rape? In order to investigate this area more thoroughly a study focusing solely on somatic reactions should be conducted.

11.5. Theoretical Considerations

The pattern of the rape-event narratives gives a picture of human sexual interaction characterized by domination, aggression and violence. The women's role is that of a prey or a scapegoat. The messages given by the offenders are loaded with ambiguity, be it the violent attacker who will later whisper tender or filthy words, or the confidence-inducing strategist who later becomes impervious to human contact, demonstrating physical dominance and sovereignty. The woman's physical safety is threatened, but above all her worth as a human being and as a woman. The behaviour of the victim is controlled by the traumatic event. The experience restricts their behaviour, their freedom to move around, to love and to interact with other people. That rape and fear of rape can be an instrument of social control over women is not conjecture when one studies the consequences of rape in the lives of the victims. In the present study the victims are mostly met with understanding from the helping profession and often also with support from close network. Efforts have been made to make that happen. But attitudes that blame the victim and reject her are also present and demonstrate that certain prejudices are alive and flourishing.

The pattern of the rape-event narratives as well as the reaction of the victimized person and others reflect the confusion surrounding the issue of rape. To be aware of these aspects enhances the ability to deal with the clinical situation.

In the first chapter, theories on the transformation of traumas into health problems are also presented. How can they be applied to the results in the present study? The investigation of rape as a stressor indicated that a rape experience includes several elements of varying importance for the victims. Serious threat to physical safety is in this study confirmed to be associated with a development of PTSD. Some of the symptoms in PTSD are closely linked to a description of what happens in classical conditioning (see chapter

1). But whereas a learning theory model might explain the reactions to stimuli associated with the event and the avoidance of these stimuli, it does not explain the intrusive re-experiencing. The numbing of responses, like loss of interest and social withdrawal, might be part of an avoidance reaction, but could also be linked to the aspect of loss of worth, control, trust or a basic assumption about life. Pierre Janet suggested that the breakdown in adaptation in relation to traumatic experiences had to do with a breakdown in the person's "cognitive schemata of the world". "The essence of psychological trauma is the loss of faith that there is order and continuity in life" (van der Kolk, 1987). This is in accord with stress theories which emphasize the importance of how the traumatic event is assessed and understood. Freud (1920) and later Horowitz (1982) view the intrusive re-experiences as reparative work, as the attempts of the psyche to understand and come to terms with what has happened. The intrusive re-experiencing may be connected with the breakdown of meaning and the attempt to process the new disturbing information.

The loss aspect is more closely connected with theories on depression (Kaplan and Saddock, 1981). The indication in the present study that long-term depression (both in combination with PTSD and alone) was linked to the degrading and shameful aspects of the traumatic experience could mean that loss of self-esteem plays a role in such a development.

The response inhibitory nature of sexual problems after rape could be explained within a learning theory model. Sexual stimuli are associated with aversive stimuli and are avoided, or sexual intercourse produces the same numbing response as was experienced during this phase of the traumatic event. Whether a theory that excludes cognitive and emotional factors related to assessment and meaning is a sufficient explanation remains to be answered.

Janet's model of dissociation and fragmentation in the information processing of traumatic events could shed light upon some of the somatic symptoms as well as some of the post-traumatic stress symptoms. "Fragments of unintegrated memories turn up as terrifying perceptions, obsessional preoccupations or somatic re-experiences", for example, pelvic pain could very well be such a somatic re-experience. Janet and Freud also believed what modern stress research has confirmed, that an extreme stress reaction may lower the threshold for physiological reactions to future stress; for example, gastro-intestinal reactions as well as increased muscular tension may be signs of such a lowered threshold.

11.6. Implications for Treatment

The results concerning both the acute post-traumatic stress reaction to rape and the predictive factors related to long-term psychiatric outcome underline the importance of recollecting and working through the traumatic experience. To go through the experience, stage by stage, pinpointing what happened, feelings and thoughts, is important for at least two reasons. The first concerns the prevention of mainly avoidance coping strategies, which may result in a phobic attitude to the memory of the event. Phobia of the memory also means phobia of reminders and will easily restrict and control the life of the victim. The results on coping in this study imply that it does not pay to try to forget before one can cope with the memory. This knowledge is not new to psychotherapists, but in work with rape victims it is astonishingly often forgotten. The victim in therapy may go to great lengths to avoid the subject of the experience itself. Most often she does not want therapeutic help after the acute crisis is over.

Another reason for working with the recollection of the trauma is to identify the distressing elements for this particular person. If the physical danger aspect is prominent, fear management, related not just to coping with the memory but also to situations and tasks she has to perform in her daily life, will be an important aspect of therapy in order to prevent long-term PTSD. If the degrading and shameful aspects are prominent, issues of shame and self-respect should be focused on in therapy in order to prevent long-term depression. Her feelings and thoughts in relation to the sexual act must be explored. If she is very depressed and there remains a strong feeling of depersonalization in the acute phase, the sexual issues in particular have to be focused upon in therapy.

Much can be said about therapeutic interventions and the difficult balance of approach and retaining control in order not to be overwhelmed. The intention here has been only to point out the possible implications for therapeutic work of the results from the present study.

References

References

Agger, I. 1989. Sexual torture of political prisoners: an overview. *Journal of Traumatic Stress*, Vol. 2, No. 3, pp. 305–308.

Agger, I. 1992. *Det blå værelse. Kvindeligt vidnesbyrd fra exiltet*. Copenhagen: Hans Reitzels Forlag.

Andenæs, J. 1974. *Alminnelig strafferett*. Oslo: Universitetsforlaget.

Andenæs, J. and Bratholm, A. 1990. *Spesiell strafferett*. Oslo: Universitetsforlaget.

Antonucci, I. C. and Depner, C. E. 1982. Social support and informal helping relationships. In T. A. Wills (ed.): *Basic Processes in Helping Relationships*. pp. 233–254.

Atkeson, B. M., Calhoun, K. S., Resick, P. A. and Ellis, E. M. 1982. Victims of rape: repeated assessment of depressive symptoms. *Journal of Couns. Clin. Psychology*, Vol. 50, No. 1, pp. 96–102.

Bang, L. 1986. *Oslo Kommunale Legevakts tilbud til pasienter utsatt for seksuelle overgrep/voldtekt. Evaluering av 6 måneders drift*. Oslo: Olso Helseråd.

Bang, L. 1988. *Voldtektsmottaket 1987*. Oslo: Oslo Kommunale Legevakt.

Bang, L., Malterud, K. and Strand, K. 1984. *Medisinsk tilbud til voldtektsofre i Oslo. En utredning om helsevesenets muligheter, begrensninger og forpliktelser*. Oslo: Oslo Helseråd.

Bartr, R. W., Lazarus, I., Luckhurstop, E. et al. 1977. Depressed lymphocyte function after bereavement. *Lancet*, Vol. 16, pp. 834–836.

Beard, R. W., Reginald, P. W. and Wadsworth, J. 1988. Clinical features of women with chronic lower abdominal pain and pelvic congestion. *Brit. J. Obst. Gynecol.*, Vol. 95, pp. 153–161.

Becker, J. V., Skinner, L. J., Gene, G. A. and Treacy, E. C. 1982. Incidence and type of sexual dysfunctions in rape and incest victims. *J. Sex Marital Ther.*, Vol. 8, No. 1, pp. 65–74.

Binder, R. 1981. Difficulties in follow-up of rape victims. *Am. J. Psychotherapy*, Vol. 35, No. 4, pp. 534–541.

Blair, I. 1985. *Investigating Rape. A New Approach for Police*. Kent: Croom Helm.

Brownmiller, S. 1974. *Against Our Will. Men, Women and Rape*. New York: Simon & Schuster.

Burgess, A. W. and Holmstrom, L. L. 1974a. Rape trauma syndrome. *Am. J. Psychiatry*, Vol. 131, pp. 1981–1986.

Burgess, A. W. and Holmstrom, L. L. 1974b. *Rape: Victims of Crisis*. Bowie, Md: Robert J. Brady Company.

Burgess, A. W. and Holmstrom, L. L. 1979a. Rape: sexual distruption and recovery. *Am. J. Orthopsychiatry*, Vol. 49, No. 4, pp. 48–57.

Burgess, A. W. and Holmstrom, L. L. 1979b. Adaptive strategies and recovery from rape. *Am. J. Psychiatry*, Vol. 136, No. 10, 1278–1282.

Burgess, A. W. and Holmstrom, L. L. 1980. Rape typology and coping behavior of rape victims. In S. L. McCombie (ed.): *Rape Crisis Intervention Handbook*. New York: Plenum Press.

Burgess, A. W. and Holmstrom, L. L. 1985. Rape Trauma Syndrome and Post Traumatic Stress Response. In A. W. Burgess (ed.): *Rape and Sexual Assault. A Research Handbook*. New York: Garland Publishing.

Burt, M. R. 1980. Cultural myths and support for rape. *Journal of Personality and Social Psychology*, Vol. 38, No. 2, pp. 217–230.

Burt, M. R. and Esteep, R. E. 1981. Apprehension and fear: learning a sense of sexual vulnerability. *Sex Roles*, Vol. 7, No. 5, pp. 511–522.

Calhoun, K. S., Atkeson, B. M. and Resick, P. A. 1982. A longitudinal examination of fear reactions in victims of rape. *J. Couns. Psychology*, Vol. 29, No. 6, pp. 655–661.

Caplan, G. 1961. *An Approach to Community Mental Health*. London: Tavistock.

Caplan, G. 1964. *Principles of Preventive Psychiatry*. New York: Basic Books.

Cobb, S. 1976. Social support as a moderator of life stress. *Psychosom. Med.*, Vol. 38, pp. 300–314.

Cohen, F. 1987. Measurements of coping. In S. V. Kasl and C. L. Copper (eds): *Stress and Health: Issues in Research Methodology*. Chichester: John Wiley & Sons.

Cohen, L. J. and Roth, S. 1987. The psychological aftermath of rape. *Journal of Social and Clinical Psychology*, Vol. 5, No. 4, pp. 825–834.

Diagnostic and Statistical Manual of Mental Disorders, DSM-III. 1980. Washington DC: American Psychiatric Association.

Diagnostic and Statistical Manual of Mental Disorders, DSM-III-R. 1987. 3rd ed. revised. Washington DC: American Psychiatric Association.

Ehrenreich, B., Hess, E. and Jacobs, G. 1987. The lust frontier. From Tupperware to sadomasochism. In *Remaking Love*. New York: Anchor Books.

Eitinger, L. and Weisæth, L. 1981. Gisselpsykiatri – en ny utfordring til psykiatrien. *Nordisk Psykiatrisk Tidsskrift*, Vol. 35, pp. 11–22.

Eitinger, L. 1985. Harald Frøshaugs minneforelesning. Viktimologi. *Tidskr. Nor. Lægeforen*, Vol. 22, No. 105, 1408–1412.

Ellis, E. M. 1983. A review of empirical rape research: victim reactions and response to treatment. *Clin. Psychology Review*, Vol. 3, pp. 473–490.

Esper, J. 1986. Reactions to violence: normal adjustment is not psychopathology. *Issues in Radical Therapy*, Vol. 12, No. 1, pp. 25–27, 52–54.

Folkman, S., Schaefer, C. and Lazarus, R. S. 1979. Cognitive processes as mediators of stress and coping. In V. Hamilton and D. M. Warburton (eds): *Human Stress and Cognition*. New York: John Wiley.

Frank, E., Turner, S. M., Stewart, B. D. Jacob, M. and West, D. 1981. Past psychiatric symptoms and the response to sexual assault. *Comprehensive Psychiatry*, Vol. 22, No. 5, pp. 479–487.

Frank, E. and Stewart, B. D. 1984. Depressive symptoms in rape victims. A revisit. *Journal of Affective Disorders*, Vol. 7, pp. 77–85.

Freud, S. 1896. Zur Äthiologie der Hysterie. In *Sigmund Freud Studienausgabe*, Vol. VI. Frankfurt am Main: Fischer Verlag GmbH, 1975.

Freud, S. 1905. *Meine Ansichteñ uber die Rolle der Sexualität in der Äthiologie der Neurosen*. In *Sigmund Freud Studienausgabe*, Vol. V. Frankfurt am Main: Fischer Verlag GmbH, 1975.

Freud, S. 1920. *Jenseits des Lustprinzips*. In *Sigmund Freud Studienausgabe*, Vol. III. Frankfurt am Main: Fischer Verlag GmbH, 1975.

Friis, S. and Vaglum, P. 1986. *Fra ide til prosjekt. En innføring i klinisk forskning*. Oslo: Tano Forlag.

Girelli, S. A., Resick, P. A. Marhoefer-Dvorak, S. and Hutter, C. K. 1986. Subjective distress and violence during rape: their effect on long-term fear. *Victims and violence*. Vol. 1, No. 1, pp. 35–45.

Goldberg, D. and Williams, P. 1988. *A User's Guide to the General Health Questionnaire.* Windsor: NFER–Nelson

Groth, N. 1977. Rape: Power, anger and sexuality. *Am. J. Psychiatry,* Vol. 134, No. 11, pp. 1239–1243.

Haan, N. 1982. The assessment of coping, defense and stress. In S. Breznitz and L. Goldberger (eds): *Handbook of Stress.* New York: The Free Press.

Hamilton, V. 1982. Cognition and stress: An information processing model. In S. Breznitz and L. Goldberger (eds): *Handbook of Stress.* New York: The Free Press.

Holen, A. 1990. *A Long-term Outcome Study of Survivors from a Disaster. The Alexander L. Kielland Disaster in Perspective.* Oslo: University of Oslo.

Holen, A., Sund, A. and Weizæth, L. 1983. *Alexander Kielland katastrofen: psykiske reaksjoner hos de overlevende. Foreløpig sluttrapport.* Oslo: University of Oslo, Division of Disaster Psychiatry.

Holmstrom, L. L. and Burgess, A. W. 1983. How we did the research. In *The Victim of Rape.* New Brunswick, NJ: Transaction Books.

Holroyd, K. and Lazarus, R. S. 1982. Stress, coping and somatic adaption. In S. Breznitz and L. Goldberger (eds): *Handbook of Stress. Theoretical and Clinical Aspects.* New York: The Free Press.

Horowitz, M. J. 1976. *Stress Response Syndromes.* New York: Jason Aronson.

Horowitz, M. J. 1982. Stress response syndromes and their treatment. In S. Breznitz and L. Goldberger (eds): *Handbook of Stress: Theoretical and Clinical Aspects.* New York: The Free Press, pp. 711–732.

Horowitz, M. J., Wilner, N. and Alvarez, W. 1979. Impact of event scale: a measure of subjective stress. *Psychosom. Med.,* Vol. 41, pp. 209–218.

Ingstad, B. and Sommerschild, H. 1983. *Familien med det funksjonshemmede barnet. Forløp – reaksjoner – mestring. Et Frambu prosjekt.* Report No. 9, Oslo.

Irwin, M., Patterson, T., Smith, T. L. et al. 1990. Reduction of immune function in life stress and depression. *Biol. Psychiatry,* Vol. 27, pp. 22–30.

Kaplan, H. and Saddock, B. J. 1981. *Modern Synopsis of Comprehensive Text-book of Psychiatry,* 3rd ed. Baltimore/London: Williams & Wilkins.

Kardiner, A. 1941. *The Traumatic Neurosis of War.* New York: P. B. Hoeber.

Katz, S. and Mazur, A. M. 1979. *Understanding the Rape Victim. A Synthesis of Research Findings.* New York: John Wiley & Son.

Keane, T. M., Fairbank, J. A., Caddell, J. M., Zimering, R. T. and Bender, M. E. 1985. A behavioral approach to assessing and treating Post-Traumatic Stress Disorder in Vietnam veterans. In C. Figley (ed): *Trauma and its Wake.* New York: Brunner/Mazel.

Kendall, M. and Stuart, A. 1977. *The Advanced Theory of Statistics.* 4th ed. London: Griffin.

Kilpatrick, D. G. 1985a. The sexual assault project: assessing the aftermath of rape. *Response,* Vol. 8, pp. 20–24.

Kilpatrick, D. G. 1985b. Mental health correlates of criminal victimization: A random community survey. *J. Consult. and Clin. Psychology,* Vol. 53, No. 6, pp. 866–873.

Kilpatrick, D. G., Resick, P. A. and Veronen, L. J. 1981. Effects of a rape experience. A longitudinal study. *Journal of Social Issues,* Vol. 37, No. 4, pp. 105–122.

Kilpatrick, D. G., Saunders, B. E., Best, C. L. and co-workers. 1989. Victim and crime factors associated with crime-related Post-Traumatic Stress Disorder. *Behaviour Therapy,* Vol. 20, pp. 199–214.

Kilpatrick, D. G., Veronen, L. J. and Resick, P. A. 1979a. The aftermath of rape: recent empirical findings. *Am. J. Orthopsychiat.,* Vol. 49, pp. 658–669.

Kilpatrick, D. G., Veronen, L. J. and Resick, P. 1979b. Assessment of the aftermath of rape: changing patterns of fear. *Journal of Behavioural Assess-ment,* Vol. 1, No. 2, pp. 133–147.

Kilpatrick, D., Veronen, L. and Resick, P. A. 1982. Psychological sequela to rape. Assessment and treatment strategies. In D. M. Doleys, Meredith and Ciminero (eds): *Behavioural Medicine: Assessment and treatment strategies.* Plenum Press, pp. 473–497.

Kilpatrick, D. G., Veronen, L. C. and Best, C. L. 1985. Factors predicting psychological distress among victims of rape. In C. R. Figley (ed.): *Trauma and its Wake.* New York: Brunner/Mazel.

Koss, M. P., Gidycz, C. A. and Wisniewski, N. 1987. The scope of rape: Incidence and prevalence of sexual aggression and victimization in a national sample of higher education students. *J. Consult and Clin. Psychology,* Vol. 55, No. 2, pp. 162–170.

Koss, M. P., Dionero, T. E. and Seibel, C. A. 1988. Stranger rape and acquaintance rape. Are there differences in the victim's experience? *Psychology of Women Quarterly,* Vol. 12, pp. 1–24.

Krupnick, J. L. and Horowitz, M. J. 1980. Victims of violence: psychological responses, treatment implications. *Evaluation and Change,* Special Issue, pp. 42–46.

Lehmann, E. L. 1975. *Nonparametric Statistical Methods Based on Ranks.* San Francisco: Holden-Day Inc.

Lewin, M. 1979. *Understanding Psychological Research.* New York: John Wiley & Sons.

Longman New Universal Dictionary. 1982. Standard edition. Harlow: Longman Group Ltd.

Lykkjen, A. M. 1976. *Voldtekt.* Oslo: Pax Forlag.

Malt, U. F. 1988. The long-term psychiatric consequences of accidental injury. *Br. J. Psychiatry,* Vol. 153, pp. 810–818.

Malt, U. F. 1989. The validity of the general health questionnaire in a sample of accidentally injured adults. *Acta psychiatr. scand.,* Suppl. 355, Vol. 80, pp. 103–112.

Malt, U. F. and Olafsen, O. M. 1992. Psychological appraisal and emotional response to physical injury: a clinical, phenomenological study of 109 adults. *Psychiatric Medicine,* Vol. 10.

Masters, W. H. and Johnson, V. 1970. *The Human Sexual Inadequacy.* Boston: Little Brown.

McGoldrick, M. and Gerson, R. 1985. *Genograms in Family Assessment.* New York: Norton and Co.

Metzger, D. 1976. It is always the woman who is raped. *Am. J. Psychiatry,* Vol. 133, No. 4, pp. 405–408.

Meyer, C. B. and Taylor, S. E. 1986. Adjustment to rape. *J. Personality and Soc. Psychol.,* Vol. 50, No. 6, pp. 1226–1234.

Mishler, E. G. 1986. The analysis of interview-narratives. In T. R. Sarbin (ed.): *Narrative Psychology. The storied nature of human conduct.* New York: Praeger.

Montgomery, S. A. and Åsberg, M. 1979. A new depression scale designed to be sensitive to change. *Brit. J. Psychiatry,* Vol. 134, pp. 382–389.

Murphy, S. M., Angelynne, E., McMullan, A., Kilpatrick, D. G. and co-workers. 1988. Rape victims' self-esteem. A longitudinal analysis. *J. Interpersonal Violence,* Vol. 3, No. 4, pp. 355–370.

Nadelson, C. C., Notman, M. T. and Carmen, E. 1986. The rape victim and the rape experience. In W. Curran (ed.): *Modern Forensic Psychiatry and Psychology.* Philadelphia: F. A. Davis.

Nadelson, C. C., Notman, M. T., Zackson, H. and Gornick, J. 1982. A follow up study of rape-victims. *Am. J. Psychiatry,* Vol. 139, No. 10, pp. 1265–1270.

Norges lover. 1983. *Straffeloven. 19de Kapitel. Forbrydelser mot sædeligheten.*

Polkinghorne, D. E. 1988a. Narrative expression. In *Narrative Knowing and the Human Sciences.* New York: State University of New York Press.

Polkinghorne, D. E. 1988b. Psychology and narrative. In *Narrative Knowing and the Human Sciences*. New York: State University of New York Press.

Rabkin, J. G. 1979. The epidemiology of forcible rape. *Am. J. Orthopsychiatry*, Vol. 49, No. 4, pp. 634–647.

Raphael, B., Lundin, T. and Weisæth, L. 1989. A research method for the study of psychological and psychiatric aspects of disaster. *Acta Psychiatr. Scand.*, Suppl. 353.

Resick, P. A., Calhoun, K. S., Atkeson, B. M. and Ellis, E. M. 1981. Social adjustment in victims of sexual assault. *J. Couns. Clin. Psychology*, Vol. 49, No. 5, 705–709.

Resick, P. A., Veronen, L. J., Kilpatrick, D. G., Calhoun, K. and Atkeson, B. M. 1986. Assessment of fear reactions in sexual assault victims: A factor analytic study of the Veronen–Kilpatrick Modified Fear Survey. *Behavioural Assessment*, Vol. 8, pp. 271–283.

Rieger, S. and Gordon, M. T. 1981. The fear of rape: a study in social control. *Journal of Social Issues*, Vol. 37, No. 4, pp. 71–92.

Rose, D. S. 1986. "Worse than death": psychodynamics of rape victims and the need for psychotherapy. *Am. J. Psychiatry*, Vol. 143, pp. 817–824.

Roth, S. and Cohen, L. J. 1986. Approach, avoidance and coping with stress. *Am. Psychologist*, Vol. 41, pp. 813–819.

Russel, D. 1983. The prevalence and incidence of forcible rape and attempted rape of females. *Victimology*, Vol. 7, pp. 81–93.

Sandanger, I., Ingebretsen, G., Sørensen, T. and Dalgard, O. S. 1992. Psykisk helse i to normal befolkninger i Norge. Paper presented at the Second Norwegian Conference on Epidemiology, Tromsø, 21 May.

Santiago, J. M., McCall-Perez, F., Gorcey, M. and Beigel, A. 1985. Long-term psychological effects of rape in 35 victims. *Am. J. Psych.*, Vol. 142, No. 11, pp. 1338–1340.

Schei, B. 1990. *Trapped in Painful Love. Physical and sexual abuse by spouse – a risk factor of gynaecological disorders and adverse perinatal outcomes.* Trondheim, Norway: University of Trondheim, Faculty of Medicine.

Seyle, H. 1982. History and present status of the stress concept. In S. Breznitz and L. Goldberg (eds): *Handbook of Stress*. New York: The Free Press.

Silverman, D. C., Kalick, M., Bowie, S. I. and Edbril, S. D. 1988. Blitz rape and confidence rape: a typology applied to 1,000 consecutive cases. *Am. J. Psychiatry*, Vol. 145, No. 11, pp. 1438–1441.

Snaith, R. P., Harrop, F. M., Newby, D. A. and Teale, C. 1986. Grade scores of the Montegomery – Åsberg Depression and the Clinical Anxiety Scales. *Brit. J. Psychiatry*, Vol. 148, pp. 599–601.

Solomon, S. D. 1986. Mobilizing social support networks in times of disaster. In C. R. Figley (ed.): *Trauma and its Wake. Vol II: Traumatic Stress, Theory, Research and Intervention*. New York: Brunner/Mazel.

Spitzer, R. L. and Williams, J. B. W. 1984. *Structured Clinical Interview for DSM-III (Scid)*, 5/1/84 revision. New York: Biometrics Research Department, New York State Psychiatric Institute.

Sørensen, T. 1991. The feeling and anticipation of social support: life stress and their impact on mental health. In *Psychiatry at the Crossroad Between Social Science and Biology*. Oslo: Norwegian University Press.

van der Kolk, B. 1987. The psychological consequences of overwhelming life experiences. In B. van der Kolk (ed.): *Psychological Trauma*. Washington: American Psychiatric Press Inc.

van der Kolk, B. 1990. The biological response to psychic trauma. Paper presented at the Second European Conference on Traumatic Stress. Norwijkerhout, The Netherlands.

van der Kolk, B. and van der Hart, O. 1989. Pierre Janet and the breakdown of

154 REFERENCES

adaption in psychological trauma. *Am. J. Psychiatry*, Vol. 146, No. 12, pp. 1530–1540.

Varvin, S. 1986. Psykososiale følger av voldstraumer – en pilotundersøkelse. *Nordisk Psykiatrisk Tidsskrift*, Vol. 40, No. 5, pp. 361–368.

Veronen, L. J. and Kilpatrick, D. G. 1980. Self-reported fears of rape-victims: A preliminary investigation. *Behaviour Modification*, Vol. 4, pp. 383–396.

Vestergaard, E. 1974. Om voldtægtsofre. Viktimologi. *Nordisk Tidsskrift for Kriminalvidenskap*, Vol. 62, pp. 151–179.

Wallace, A. F. C. 1956. *Tornado in Worcester: an explanatory study of individual and collective behaviour in an extreme situation*. Washington: National Academy of Sciences, National Research Council, No. 166.

Weisæth, L. and Sund, A. 1982. Psychiatric problems in UNIFIL and the UN-soldiers stress syndrome. *Revue Internationale des Services de Santé*, Vol. 55, pp. 109–116.

Weisæth, L. 1984. *Stress Reactions to an Industrial Disaster*. Oslo: Medical Faculty, University of Oslo.

Weisæth, L. 1989. Torture of a Norwegian ship's crew. The torture, stress reactions and psychiatric after-effects. *Acta psychiatr. Scand.*, Suppl. 355, Vol. 80, pp. 63–72.

Weisæth, L. 1991. Post-traumatisk stressforstyrrelse. En ny diagnose. *Sandoz-informasjon*, Vol. 4, pp. 3–9.

Åsberg, M., Perris, C., Schalling, D. and Sedwall, G. 1978. The CPRS: development and applications of a psychiatric rating scale. *Acta Psych. Scand.*, Suppl. 271.